116 FAVORITE TANTALIZING GOOD-HEALTH RECIPES

BY

Marti Wheeler

Copyright 1984 Marti Wheeler Fry

TABLE OF CONTENTS

INTRODUCTION

What could be more exciting than enjoying the most delicious and satisfying of all foods while simultaneously becoming healthier, slimmer and more energetic than ever before? This book will enable you to do it all!

You are about to discover the easiest and simplest method of food preparation (aside from no preparation at all)! In addition, you will be relieved from the tedious and time-consuming chore of heavy dishwashing. (Everything can be rinsed with plain water—no detergents necessary!) *All* your work in the kitchen will be easier, quicker and cleaner!

Despite the surprising ease of food preparation and after-meal cleanup, your meals will be tastier and more wholesome than those you are accustomed to eating. And, the benefit of benefits: you will come to experience greater health and well-being, few (if any) sicknesses, and a higher level of energy. If you need to lose a few (or many) pounds, they'll melt away like magic!

By now you may be wondering what the trick is. So I'll tell you: The recipes in this book utilize primarily *uncooked foods*. Most of the recipes are *all-raw*! But before you turn away in disappointment—try them out. I'm certain you'll be pleasantly surprised. About half of the salad and main-course recipes contain cooked ingredients, along with an abundance of uncooked ingredients. For maximum flavor and healthfulness (funny how deliciousness and wholesomeness can go hand-in-hand!), cooked ingredients are either lightly steamed or baked. Thus even cooking pans are easy to clean!

The second trick to obtaining exquisite taste thrills while simultaneously becoming healthier than you ever thought possible is to eschew condiments and seasonings. Again, before you close this book and let it gather dust, try it out! Once your taste buds become accustomed to the wide range of natural food flavors, and once they become unaddicted to salt, vinegar, sugar, honey, and seasonings, you'll discover taste pleasures you never knew were possible.

But why eschew salt, sweeteners, vinegar and seasonings? Though few people know it, these "flavor enhancers" are extremely unhealthful. Along with meats and dairy foods, they introduce poisonous, irritating, unwholesome, disease-causing toxins into your body. Basically, it is these, along with drugs, fried foods, animal foods and lack of exercise, sleep, fresh air, etc., that *cause*

3

diseases, lethargy and overweight. Remove the causes of disease, overweight and lethargy, and you remove the disease! With disease absent, you will naturally become slim and energetic!

(Note: Some of the recipes in this book contain nonsalt vegetable seasonings to help you make the transition from your present dietary style to this new healthful way of eating.)

If all this sounds too simple to be true, don't be fooled. The most sophisticated, complex, expensive methods utilizing drugs, surgery and other debilitating treatments are ineffective. Millions continue to suffer terribly from the results of eating condiments and unwholesome foods (coupled with inadequate exercise, rest, sleep, and fresh air). Drugs and herbs palliate symptoms, but sicknesses, diseases and ailments are not truly overcome until their causes are removed. We cannot continue to indulge the causes of disease and lethargy and expect to have health or energy!

So, if you want to be superbly healthy and energetic and simultaneously enjoy the most delicious of all foods, plus appreciate the extra time- and labor-saving benefits of easy food preparation and effortless dishwashing, keep this book in your kitchen—and use it!

BECOME A CULINARY ARTIST

The recipes begin with a list of all the ingredients used in the recipe. After this listing are the instructions for making the dish.

You will notice, however, that very few recipes tell you *how much* of each ingredient to use. It would have been a very easy matter to do so, but *you* can just as easily decide quantities. There's nothing tricky or magical about it! No matter how much or little you use of each ingredient (within reason), the recipe will taste great because the ingredients and combinations in it are delicious!

The advantages of deciding for yourself how much of each ingredient to add are numerous. For one, you can be more creative. The more creative you are, the more fun you will have preparing meals. Instead of preparing food like a robot, you'll do it as a culinary artist! Even if you don't consider yourself creative, you'll be surprised to find that you are after all.

A second advantage of *your* deciding how much to use of each ingredient is that you will discover each recipe to be several recipes in one. In other words, by varying the quantities (and possibly deleting or adding one or more ingredients), you will create new recipes on your own!

Thirdly, by deciding for yourself how much of each item to use, you can maximally please your (and your family's or friends') palates. For example, in the Springtime Fruit Salad, blueberry lovers can go extra-heavy on the blueberries. If you have only one ripe mango, that's okay, or you can use lots of them if you have them and love them (most people do!). If you're not wild about apples (or can't get hold of organic ones and prefer not to have to peel sprayed ones), you can either leave the apples out or use a smaller portion of them. If you wish, you can go heavier on the bananas.

In addition, how much you use of each ingredient depends, not only on how many people are being served, but also on the size of their appetites and what else (if anything) is being served with the dish. Thus overall amounts, as well as proportions, can vary significantly.

Feel free to experiment with the recipes given here. They are meant to be sample recipes and guidelines so you can then go ahead and create your own according to your taste preferences, what's available to you, etc. When you do, keep in mind the food combining guidelines as follows:

HEALTHFUL AND DELICIOUS FOOD COMBINATIONS

The ingredients used in the recipes are selected to combine with all other ingredients in the recipe. But what do I mean when I say that? Your health and well-being are of primary importance. Thus none of the ingredients used in a recipe interfere with the efficient digestion of any of the other ingredients. As a result, food does *not* stay in your stomach and decompose into harmful bacterial decomposition waste products. And this is good for your health!

In fact, faulty digestion due to the helter-skelter food combinations customarily eaten is a significant contributor to disease and lethargy. So you can see how important it is to combine foods for efficient digestion!

Many combinations taste great together but are not digested well if eaten together. For best results in improving your health and eating enjoyment, you should stay within the food combining guidelines given in this section. Fortunately, even though certain tasty combinations are *not* healthful and are therefore *not* used, the healthful combinations that *are* used are enticingly delicious. So you won't miss any titillating taste pleasures!

Foods Classified

To establish guidelines for combining foods for efficient digestion, we must first categorize foods according to their most prominent dietary character.

One food classification is *protein*. High-protein foods included in this book are nuts, seeds and beans. Other high-protein foods (not recommended) include cheeses, eggs, meats, and fish. Protein digestion requires the enzyme pepsin, secreted in the stomach in hydrochloric acid. (Carnivores such as dogs secrete far more and stronger hydrochloric acid than do humans. Therefore, they are able to efficiently digest flesh, whereas we are not. Thus meat is healthful for them but results in putrefaction [protein decomposition] and diseases in humans.)

A second food classification is *starch*. The starches used (or that could be used) in this book include potatoes, corn, peas, yams, squash, rice, and legumes (beans). Other starches (*not* recommended) are breads, pasta (noodles), and flour and flour products such as cakes, cookies, corn tortillas and chips. Starches are digested by the enzyme ptyalin, secreted in the saliva and the pancreas. Ptyalin is active in an alkaline medium and is destroyed in acids. Thus starches should not be eaten with proteins, since proteins signal secretion of hydrochloric acid, which halts starch digestion.

A third food classification is nonstarchy vegetables. It includes foods such as lettuces, cabbages, alfalfa sprouts, cucumbers, eggplant, turnips, green corn, green beans, kohlrabi, okra, fresh peas, yellow crookneck squash, zucchini, celery, Brussel sprouts, broccoli, sweet peppers, bok choy, kale, collards, etc. (A few vegetables are not as starchy as potatoes and yams but are considered mildly starchy. These include carrots, rutabagas, cauliflower, and beets. For practical purposes, we include them with the nonstarchy vegetables.) The nonstarchy vegetables we do *not* recommend are those that contain harmful poisons (irritants): onions, horseradishes, garlic, leeks, radishes, hot peppers, chives, etc. Because of their neutral character, nonstarchy and mildly starchy vegetables can be combined either with proteins (nuts and seeds) or with starches (potatoes, yams, rice, etc.).

A fourth food category is fats. The healthful fats are avocados, nuts, seeds and coconuts. The unhealthful ones (not recommended) are butter, oils, lard, etc. Since oils digest rather slowly, they are best eaten with nonstarchy vegetables but not with proteins, starches or fruits. Avocados, since they do not contain as much protein as nuts and seeds, may be eaten with starches such as potatoes and yams as a natural butter.

A fifth basic food classification is fruits. Many people can eat all kinds of fruits together with little if any digestive problems. Others, who, due to traditional eating practices, have impaired gastrointestinal tracts and digestive capabilities have discomforts if they combine fruits without consideration for the differences between the four categories of fruits. (Unfortunately, some people have digestive troubles no matter how they combine their foods. However, these problems will eventually clear up if they follow the food combining guidelines and other recommendations given in this book.)

The fruits can be categorized either as sweet fruits, subacid fruits, acid fruits, or melons. People with digestive troubles are advised to eat melons alone (as a mono meal); to combine sweet fruits with one another and with subacid fruits; and to combine acid fruits with one another and with subacid fruits. The sweet fruits include bananas, papayas, all dried fruits, cherimoyas, sapotes, mangoes, raisins, persimmons and sweet grapes. The acid fruits include citrus fruits (grapefruits, oranges, lemons, limes, tangerines), pineapples, strawberries, sour plums, sour berries and any other very tart or sour fruits. The subacid fruits include apples, peaches, pears, grapes, plums, apricots, blueberries, nectarines, and cherries.

The most important thing to keep in mind when combining fruits is to eat them separately from all other foods. In other words, eat fruits at all-fruit meals. The reason for this is that fruit sugars require no digestion. Therefore, they are passed speedily to the intestines for absorption of their fine sugars. If slower-digesting foods such as proteins, starches or fats are eaten with fruits, however, they are held up in the stomach where their sugars ferment. Poisonous fermentation by-products harm us and also interfere with protein or starch digestion. This guideline is easier to follow than you might think because all-fruit meals are fantastically delicious, nutritious and easy to prepare!

Food Combining Guidelines

Combining foods for efficient digestion is a snap! With a few basic guidelines to follow, you can start *now* to have better health, more energy and zero digestive disturbances!
1. Eat proteins and starches at separate meals.
2. Eat proteins with nonstarchy vegetables.
3. Eat starches with nonstarchy vegetables.
4. Eat fats with nonstarchy vegetables. (Avocados may also be eaten with starches.)
5. Eat fruits at all-fruit meals. If you have digestive problems:
   a. Eat melons alone.
   b. Eat sweet fruits with subacid fruits.
   c. Eat acid fruits with subacid fruits.

Eating mono meals of just one kind of fruit is a good practice, especially for your first meal of the day. This allows easiest digestion. Simple compatible combinations of just two or three kinds of foods at one meal is also tastier and more healthful than mixtures of many kinds of foods. For example, bananas and dates; grapes and dried figs; or apples and soaked dried apricots are all excellent meals. Likewise, avocados with lettuce and tomatoes makes a fine easily-digestible meal.

Speaking of tomatoes, they are technically acid fruits. However, since they don't have the sugar content of citrus and other acid fruits, they can be eaten with proteins or fats. However, they shouldn't be eaten with starches because of the previously-stated fact that acids destroy the starch-splitting enzyme, ptyalin. (Likewise, dressings containing lemon or lime juice [or other acids] should not be used with a starch meal.) Dressings of or containing lemon, lime or grapefruit juices may be used with fats or proteins, since there is a relatively small amount of sugar in dressing-size portions of these juices.

FOOD COMBINING CHART

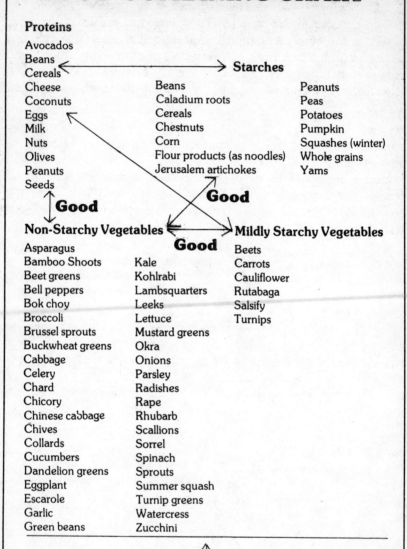

Proteins

Avocados
Beans
Cereals
Cheese
Coconuts
Eggs
Milk
Nuts
Olives
Peanuts
Seeds

Starches

Beans
Caladium roots
Cereals
Chestnuts
Corn
Flour products (as noodles)
Jerusalem artichokes

Peanuts
Peas
Potatoes
Pumpkin
Squashes (winter)
Whole grains
Yams

Good

Good

Non-Starchy Vegetables

Good

Mildly Starchy Vegetables

Asparagus
Bamboo Shoots
Beet greens
Bell peppers
Bok choy
Broccoli
Brussel sprouts
Buckwheat greens
Cabbage
Celery
Chard
Chicory
Chinese cabbage
Chives
Collards
Cucumbers
Dandelion greens
Eggplant
Escarole
Garlic
Green beans

Kale
Kohlrabi
Lambsquarters
Leeks
Lettuce
Mustard greens
Okra
Onions
Parsley
Radishes
Rape
Rhubarb
Scallions
Sorrel
Spinach
Sprouts
Summer squash
Turnip greens
Watercress
Zucchini

Beets
Carrots
Cauliflower
Rutabaga
Salsify
Turnips

Poor

Fruits, Sugars and Syrups

Fruits are best eaten alone or with each other. Sugars or syrups, if eaten, are best eaten only with fruits. (Lettuce and celery may be eaten with fruits, as they are very neutral vegetables.)

RATING THE RECIPES

You've probably seen the five- to one-star rating system for movies on TV. The best movies are rated five stars and the worst rate one. I've adopted this same rating system to judge the relative healthfulness of the recipes in this book.

Recipes of healthful raw foods, all compatibly combined and with no condiments are rated with five stars. One star is subtracted for cooked ingredients; one is subtracted for any incompatible combinations; and one is subtracted for the use of condiments or seasonings.

Hence, recipes with one or more cooked ingredients but with no condiments or incompatible combinations are rated with four stars; compatibly-combined all-raw recipes with condiments are rated four stars; and all-raw recipes that have one or more incompatible combinations but no condiments are rated four stars.

Three-star recipes are those either that have one or more incompatible combinations plus condiments or cooked ingredients *or* that have cooked ingredients plus condiments or one or more incompatible combinations.

Recipes that have condiments, incompatible combinations *and* cooked ingredients are rated three stars; and recipes that also have less wholesome ingredients are rated two stars (unless the less wholesome ingredient[s] are listed as optional).

One-star ratings are reserved for recipes that are furthest from ideal in all respects.

LUSCIOUS FRUIT SALADS

Why save the best for last when you can have the best first and last!?!! For optimum health and energy, make full meals on ripe fresh fruits. They're *far* more nutritious than most people realize. The natural sugars in fresh fruits are not the least bit harmful. In fact, they fill our carbohydrate (energy) needs in the most delicious and easily-digestible form.

No need to fear constipation when fresh fruits comprise the bulk of your diet! If you're concerned about diarrhea or loose stools from eating much fruit, keep in mind that this will occur only if your body is toxic—and then only temporarily until your body has fully purified itself—and is kept pure. In the meantime, if you have loose stools, wait patiently and it will pass. After all, it's only a minor temporary discomfort in preparation for health and energy like you've never known before!

Tantalizing Tropical Fruits

The best-known tropical fruit is the banana. Did you know there are numerous varieties of bananas? These are available only in the tropical countries where they grow, though you may occasionally see some red finger bananas on your supermarket shelves.

The papaya is probably in second place when it comes to familiarity. Yellow and soft when ripe, this delectable pear-shaped tropical fruit has a delicate melony flavor. It is superbly delicious eaten as is. For variety, you may wish to fill the cavity of each papaya half with sliced fresh fruit or fruit salad. Or eat it with a little lime juice! Fresh papaya chunks or slices also make a fine garnish for puddings, soups, or fruit or vegetable salads. Or try it liquefied in your blender with fresh-squeezed orange juice! Fantastic!

One of the most popular fruits worldwide is the mango. Like the papaya, it is soft and beautifully orange/yellow/red (depending on the variety) when ripe. The mango is one of the most delicious of all fruits!

Like bananas and papayas, you do not eat the skins of mangoes. Also, they have large oblong pits. Simply cut or scrape the flesh away from pits and eat as is or cut up in a fresh fruit salad or fruit soup. Or use it as a garnish or blended with apple, orange or grape juice in a tasty fruit blend.

A third luscious tropical fruit that is becoming ever more popular is the kiwifruit. It is small and fuzzy brown on the outside, but, surprise! It's a brilliant emerald-green inside! In fact, when you slice it crosswise, the (edible) black seeds create a gorgeous sunburst design!

Also called the New Zealand or Chinese Gooseberry, the kiwifruit is excitingly delicious when soft-ripe. You may peel, slice or dice and add to salads, or halve and scoop out the flesh with a spoon. The beautiful kiwi makes a lovely decoration for garnishing most any dish!

TRUDY'S FRUIT SALAD * * * * *

For one large serving:

1 lg. ripe mango
4 speckled bananas
3 ripe peaches

1. Peel mango with a sharp knife, or quarter around pit and pull peeling off by hand.
2. Dice mango flesh into large bowl and scrape flesh away from the pit with a sharp knife.
3. Peel and cut *two* of the four bananas into bowl.
4. Wash, dice and add peaches.
5. Peel and liquefy remaining two bananas on high blender speed.
6. Pour banana dressing over cut-up fruits and stir together well.
7. Serve and savor!

HOW TO PREPARE A PINEAPPLE

Since nice ripe Hawaiian pineapples are scrumptious in fruit salads, you will need to know how to prepare them. Here are easy-to-follow instructions:

1. Using a sharp knife and a cutting board, cut off top of pineapple.
2. Quarter fruit lengthwise and slice the core off each quarter.
3. Sample pineapple at the end where you cut off the top. Cut off the portion (if any) that lacks flavor and sweetness (may be 1-2 inches or more). This sour portion can be liquefied with a few pitted dates to make a delicious fruit salad dressing.
4. Separate fruit from husk by undercutting each quarter between fruit and the husk with the sharp tip of your knife. Undercut all the way around each quarter.
5. Leaving undercut fruit on husks, cut fruit into bite-sized pieces by cutting vertically and horizontally down to (but not through) the husk.
6. Slide pineapple chunks into large salad bowl and, with the tip of a teaspoon, scrape pineapple remaining on the husk into bowl.

FRUIT MEDLEY * * * * *

Peaches
Oranges
Pineapple
Red and Yellow Delicious apples
White seedless grapes
Strawberries
Bananas

1. Wash peaches, apples, grapes, and strawberries and peel oranges and bananas. (Nonorganic apples should be peeled.)
2. De-stem strawberries and cut all fruits into bite-sized pieces. Grapes can be left whole.
3. Toss together in a large bowl and serve. (A cup or large ladle works best for serving.)

SOAKING DRIED FRUITS

Raisins and other dried fruits may be used in fruit salads either dry or soaked. I prefer them soaked by far. Here's how to soak dried fruits:

1. Place dried fruit in a bowl or other container.
2. Add just enough distilled water to cover fruit.
3. Cover container and allow to stand several hours or overnight at room temperature.
4. If you keep soaked fruit longer than 12 or so hours, store in the refrigerator so it won't ferment. (Soaked fruit keeps in the refrigerator about 3-4 days at most.)

TERRY FRY'S FRUIT SALAD * * * * *

To make four servings:
1 pineapple (minus sour portion, if any)
4 soft kiwi fruits
Juice of 4 oranges
1 banana
2 handsful (soaked) raisins
2 sm. stalks celery
1 qt. (2 pts.) strawberries

1. Prepare pineapple and place in large bowl.
2. Peel kiwi fruits (or halve and scoop out flesh with a teaspoon).
3. Cut up kiwis and halve and juice oranges.
4. Peel and cut up banana.
5. Place all ingredients in bowl, along with raisins (soaked or unsoaked) and washed and diced celery.
6. Wash, de-stem and cut up strawberries; add strawberries to bowl; and thoroughly mix all ingredients together.
7. Serve large portions as a full meal.

A plate of washed lettuce leaves may be served along with this (or any) fruit salad. If you wish, you may place spoonsful of salad down the middle or large lettuce leaves and roll up or fold over and eat as a fruit sandwich!

CANDIED STRAWBERRY SALAD *****

Serves two:
3 lg. ripe bananas
1½ lg. (or 2 sm.) organic Yellow Delicious apples
1 pt. strawberries
10-15 dates

1. Peel and slice bananas; wash and dice apples (whether organic or not); wash and de-stem strawberries; and pit dates.
2. Liquefy half the strawberries in a blender, add pitted dates, and liquefy again.
3. Place all ingredients in a large bowl, mix together well, and serve.

SUMMERTIME FRUIT SALAD *****

Blueberries
Mangos
Apples
Bananas

1. Peel mangos with a sharp knife, or quarter around the pit and peel off the skin by hand.
2. Slice mango flesh away from pits into a bowl, and scrape pits with knife to remove fruit that sticks to them.
3. Using a sharp knife, cut up mangos in the bowl.
4. Wash blueberries; wash, quarter, core and dice apples; peel and slice bananas; and mix all ingredients together.

17

WALDORF SALAD *****

Apples and/or pears
Raisins, soaked or unsoaked
Celery
Dried apricots, soaked or not
Peaches
Lettuce and/or cabbage (optional)

1. Wash, quarter, core, and dice apples and/or pears.
2. Wash and dice celery; wash and cut or break up lettuce; and/or grate cabbage.
3. Wash and dice up peaches and dried apricots. (The apricots are much softer and moister if they have been allowed to soak overnight or several hours in distilled water. The same goes for the raisins.)
4. Peel, pit and mash peaches.
5. Mix all ingredients together in a large bowl.

If you prefer, you may use whole lettuce or cabbage leaves on plates under the salad mixture instead of mixed in. Or serve whole lettuce or cabbage leaves on the side to eat as is or with fruit salad rolled in them as sandwiches.

PINEAPPLE-STRAWBERRY SALAD WITH PECANS ****

For 3-4 servings:

1 lg. Hawaiian pineapple
2 pts. fresh strawberries
1 pt. other berries (blackberries, dewberries, mulberries, blueberries, raspberries, etc. [optional])
3-5 Navel oranges (optional)
8-12 oz. shelled pecans

1. Prepare pineapple and place in a large bowl.
2. Wash, de-stem and cut up strawberries.
3. Wash other berries (if you use them).
4. If you're using Navel oranges, peel, section, and cut each section into halves or thirds.
5. Place berries and oranges in bowl with pineapple.
6. Pecans may be used whole, chopped or ground. Add them to salad bowl and mix all ingredients together well.

FRUITY-TOOTIE SALAD * * * * *

Red Delicious apples
Golden Delicious apples
Ripe bananas
Dried pineapple (without sugar or honey), soaked
Monukka raisins, soaked

1. Peel apples if not organic; then quarter, core, and dice apples.
2. Peel and cut up bananas, and cut up dried pineapple.
3. Mix these ingredients in a large bowl with soaked raisins. (Thompson raisins may be substituted for Monukka.)
4. Pour soak water into salad, drink it separately, or use it in the following dressing:

Soak water from raisins
Ripe bananas

1. Peel bananas and liquefy in blender with soak water.
2. Pour over salad and mix in well.

JANUARY'S FRUIT SALAD * * * * *

To make 1-2 servings:
¾ c. soaked dried apricots or figs
2 bananas
1 pear
1 lg. Rome apple

1. Pour apricot or fig soak water into blender, along with *one-half* banana. Liquefy on high speed. This is the salad dressing!
2. Peel remaining 1-½ bananas and slice into a large salad bowl.
3. Wash, core, and dice pear and apple, peeling the apple before dicing it (even if it's organic).
4. Place dried fruit and salad dressing in salad bowl with bananas; cut up and add soaked dried apricots or figs; and mix all ingredients together well.

STRAWBERRY-RAISIN SALAD *****

For two servings:
1 c. raisins, soaked
1-½ pints strawberries
2 lg. apples
3 bananas

1. Pour raisin soak water into blender and add *one* banana.
2. Liquefy blender contents on high speed to make a fruit salad dressing. Set aside.
3. Wash and de-stem strawberries; cut into halves or quarters, depending upon their size; and place in a large mixing bowl, along with washed, quartered, cored, peeled, and diced apples and sliced bananas.
4. Pour in raisins and dressing, mix together well, serve, and enjoy!

ZESTY FRUIT SALAD WITH DRESSING *****

For eight servings:
½ lg. pineapple, cubed (about 2-½ c.)
3-4 papayas, cubed (about 2 c.)
4-6 kiwifruits, peeled and cubed (about 1 c.)
1 c. strawberry halves
1 banana
½ c. freshly-squeezed orange juice

1. In a large bowl combine pineapple, papaya, kiwifruit, and strawberries.
2. In a blender combine banana and orange juice until smooth.
3. Pour blender contents over fruit and mix gently.

PINEAPPLE-BERRY SALAD *****

For 3-4 servings:

1 good-sized Hawaiian pineapple
2 pts. fresh strawberries
1 pt. dewberries, blackberries, mulberries,
  raspberries, blueberries,
  or other berries as available
3 Navel oranges (optional)

1. Prepare pineapple; de-stem, wash and cut up strawberries; and wash other berries.
2. Place fruits in a large bowl.
3. Peel and section Navel oranges (if you're using them); cut each section into halves or thirds; and add to mixing bowl.
4. Thoroughly mix all ingredients and serve as an entire meal. Super-delicious!

FABULOUS FRUIT DRESSINGS / DIPS / SPREADS / TOPPINGS

Fruit salads are so delicious that they really don't need dressings like most vegetable salads do. However, dressings coat all the individual fruits in a salad, making the salad a cohesive unit and providing a nice flavor, texture and appearance.

The sample recipes given here are meant to give you ideas and get you started. Once you've made these sample recipes, you'll probably be off and running with numerous dressings of your own creation. And, once you see how easy fruit salad dressings are to make, and how delicious they taste, you'll whip them up effortlessly and without a second thought. All you need is a blender or food processor, though some fruit dressings can be made by mashing bananas, other soft fresh fruits, soaked dried fruits, and/or juices with a fork or potato masher.

In addition to mixing fruit dressings into fruit salads, you can use them as dips, spreads, or toppings. To use as dips, simply serve in a bowl or cups, along with one or more kinds of sliced or halved fruits (apples, pears, bananas, peaches, plums, etc.). Or use as a spread on fruit sandwiches (banana and/or other fruit slices wrapped in large Romaine or Leaf lettuce leaves). And, all-Natural Banana Ice Cream, while super-good by itself, is even better with sliced bananas and a fruit salad dressing as a topping!

EASY BANANA DRESSING *****

Bananas

1. Peel and halve (very ripe) bananas and place half a banana in blender.
2. Blend on high speed until liquefied, and then add more banana halves and liquefy again.
3. Stop blender and mash bananas against blades when/if necessary.
4. Continue until all bananas are blended.

PERFECT PEAR DRESSING/DIP *****

Dried pears
Fresh pears (optional)
Bananas

1. Soak dried pears overnight in distilled water.
2. Pour soaked pears and soak water into blender.
3. If you're using fresh pears, quarter, core, peel and add them.
4. Peel and add bananas and liquefy all ingredients together well.

PEACHY BANANA DRESSING OR DIP *****

4-5 peaches
2 bananas

1. Wash and pit peaches; place in blender; and liquefy on high speed.
2. Peel bananas; break them in half; and liquefy with blended peaches until smooth and creamy.
3. If necessary, stop blender, remove cover, and mash and stir contents with a fork or spoon; then replace cover and liquefy again.
4. Serve in small bowls as a dip for wedges of apples, pears, and other fresh fruits; or pour over a large bowl of cut-up fruits as a fruit salad dressing and stir well.

APRICOT SALAD DRESSING *****

Dried and/or fresh apricots
Distilled water

1. Soak dried apricots in distilled water overnight or several hours.
2. If you have fresh apricots, wash and pit them.
3. Blend apricots with soak water on high speed. If necessary, add a little more distilled water.

SATISFYING MAIN-COURSE SALADS

Vegetables and nuts, second only to fruits, are of central importance in a healthful diet. Vegetables have far more flavor, crispness, body, and nutrients when eaten raw in salads than when cooked. Vegetable salads are especially delicious—as well as satisfying—when eaten with nuts, seeds, avocados, and/or a tasty homemade salad dressing.

Greens, sprouts, other vegetables, nuts, seeds, and avocados are extremely rich in vitamins, minerals, and essential fatty acids, in addition to supplying plenty of high-quality usable protein. In addition, they provide variety from the sweet taste of fruits. However, keep in mind that you will feel far better and more energetic if at least half to two-thirds of your diet consists of fruits, because fruits supply our foremost nutrient need—glucose—with the least digestive and toxic burden, as well as a broad array of vitamins, minerals, amino acids, and essential fatty acids.

For the most flavor and least toxins, buy organically-grown foods whenever possible. Or, better yet, grow your own. Every landowner should grow fruit trees, vine fruits, and vegetables; and renters should grow vegetables if at all possible—or at least sprouts. In addition, learn how to select the best-quality food, and use it while it's fresh. Eating in is far healthier too, as restaurants (except for some health-oriented or vegetarian ones) use more chemicals (sulfites, etc.), salt, rancid oils, etc., then you would use at home.

The first half of the following recipes are for all-raw, main-course salads, most of which include nuts, seeds or avocados to make them particularly rich, tasty, and satisfying. The second half of the main-course salad recipes contain one cooked vegetable, along with the usual uncooked salad veggies.

SESAME SALAD SUPREME * * * * *

For 3-4 servings:
Lettuce, preferably Romaine
Celery
Cauliflower
Cucumbers
3-6 tomatoes
Dulse (optional)
Alfalfa sprouts
8-12 oz. sesame seeds

1. Wash and dry lettuce and break it up into a large bowl.
2. Wash and dice celery and place it and cauliflowerettes in the bowl, along with peeled and diced cucumbers and washed and cut up tomatoes.
3. Add lots of alfalfa sprouts and toss.
4. Grind sesame seeds, either in a nut and seed grinder, a hand grinder, or a blender; and add to large salad bowl.
5. Place several large ripe tomatoes, quartered, in blender and liquefy.
6. While blender is running, add a couple cut-up stalks of washed celery, a large peeled and quartered cucumber (and well-rinsed dulse if desired) through opening in blender lid.
7. Blend on high speed until all ingredients are liquefied.
8. Pour blender contents into the salad bowl and mix everything together well.

25

NUTTY BROCCOLI SALAD

Broccoli
Celery
Cherry tomatoes
Pignolias
Pecans
Lemon juice

1. Wash and cut up broccoli and celery, using twice as much broccoli as celery.
2. Wash and halve a fairly large quantity of cherry tomatoes.
3. Chop pecans and juice about ½ lemon for every two people being served.
4. Place all ingredients in a large bowl and mix well.
5. Alfalfa and other sprouts can be placed on top of each serving if desired.

This salad is a meal in itself. It can be eaten as is or served with a plateful of washed whole lettuce leaves (Leaf or Romaine are good) as a lettuce sandwich filling. Provide plates for making and setting sandwiches on.

THE BEST VEGEMOLE * * * *

Delight guests with this very special version of Mexican guacamole!

This recipe is particularly handy in wintertime when the varieties of avocados on the market are not as tasty as at other times of the year. The four-star rating is because of the shallot and parsley used. Both are less than ideal foods due to their toxin content. (They do add a magic touch, flavorwise, however!) The kelp also contributes to the four-star rating because it is not a fresh whole food but a flavoring that is obtained through processing.

Avocados
A grapefruit
A lime
½ sm shallot
Powdered or granulated kelp
Red (or green) cabbage
Broccoli
Celery
Fresh parsley
Tomatoes

Tomatillos (optional)
Fresh cilantro (optional)
Dash of Nature's Gourmet (or other salt-free
  vegetable seasoning) (optional)

1. Peel and quarter avocados; and, using a fork, mash avocados on a plate. Set aside any avocados that you quartered but discovered were too hard to mash up easily.
2. Juice grapefruit and lime into blender.
3. Add one-half small shallot (or comparable amount of scallion, chives or wild onion), some kelp (and a dash of Nature's Gourmet or other seasoning, if you're using it) to fruit juices in blender.
4. If any of the avocados are not soft enough to mash up easily, add them to blender also.
5. Liquefy blender contents on high speed and mix with mashed avocado in a large bowl.
6. Cut up cabbage, broccoli, celery, parsley, tomatoes, tomatillos (if you're using them) and cilantro (if you're using it).
7. Add cut-up vegetables to avocado mixture and stir well.
8. Serve with whole celery stalks and lettuce leaves, using as a dip for celery and as a "filling" for lettuce "sandwiches." Alfalfa sprouts may be put on top or mixed in.

CHINESE CABBAGE SALAD * * * * *

For two servings:

8 leaves Chinese cabbage
2 red bell peppers
2 avocados
1 pt. cherry tomatoes
  (or 3 regular tomatoes)
1 grapefruit

1. Wash and dry Chinese cabbage; cut up four of the leaves; and place in a large mixing bowl.
2. Place remaining four leaves on two dinner plates.
3. Wash and dice red bell peppers; and quarter, peel and dice avocados (or halve avocados and scoop out flesh with a teaspoon).
4. Place peppers and avocados, along with washed and halved (or diced) tomatoes, in mixing bowl.
5. Juice grapefruit and pour juice over ingredients in mixing bowl.
6. Stir well and place a dallop of salad on each of the four Chinese cabbage leaves on the dinner plates.
7. Serve remaining salad in bowls—and you have a full meal!

PECAN SALAD * * * * *

Lettuce, kale, collards, other greens
Celery
Tomatoes
Bell peppers, sweet red or green
Cucumbers
Broccoli
Turnips
Brussel sprouts
Alfalfa sprouts
Mung sprouts (optional)
Ground pecans

1. Wash, cut up and combine all or some of the above-listed ingredients and serve. (Turnips need to be peeled first.)
2. The more ground pecans you use (up to four ounces per serving), the more filling and satisfying this salad will be.

VEGETARIAN HUM-DINGER SALAD * * * * *

Romaine (or other) lettuce
Chinese cabbage
Tomatoes
Avocados
Tomatillos, if available
Grapefruit, ½ per serving
Brussel sprouts, 2 per serving
Broccoli
Sunflower sprouts, 2 per serving
Sunflower seeds, 3-4 oz. per serving
Sunflower, lentil or other sprouts (optional)
Fresh parsley (optional)

1. Break or cut up lettuce and Chinese cabbage, dice tomatoes (or halve cherry tomatoes), and chop parsley very finely (if you're using it).
2. Quarter, peel (by hand) and dice avocados; remove outer coverings from tomatillos; and finely dice tomatillos.
3. Halve and juice grapefruit(s) and dice Brussel sprouts.
4. Wash and cut up broccoli.
5. Add sunflower seeds (and sprouts, if desired.) (Sunflower sprouts should be cut up a little for easy eating.)
6. Stir all ingredients together well and serve as a meal in itself (or alongside a bowl of vegetable soup).

PIGNOLIA-SUNFLOWER SALAD *****

For two servings:

3-4 oz. pignolia nuts,
 preferably Chinese pignolias
3-4 oz. sunflower seeds
Lettuce
Celery
Sunflower sprouts (optional)
Alfalfa sprouts (optional)
Cucumbers (optional)

1. Wash, dry and break up lettuce into a large bowl.
2. Wash and dice celery.
3. If you're using cucumbers, peel them or not, depending on your preference and whether they're waxed or not (waxed cucumbers should be peeled).
4. If you're using sunflower sprouts, cut them up, and, if you're using alfalfa sprouts, break them up so they're not clumpy.
5. Toss these ingredients with pignolia nuts and sunflower seeds.
6. This salad can be served with or without a dressing. A simple, compatible dressing can be made from a blend of pignolias or sunflower seeds, celery and tomatoes:

---

   a. Wash and quarter tomatoes [or use cherry tomatoes whole] and liquefy on highest blender speed.
   b. Wash, cut up and, with blender running, add and liquefy with blended tomatoes.
   c. Add nuts or seeds the same way, with the blender running, until dressing is thick and smooth. [Turn blender off and on as needed, stopping to stir if necessary, and blending again.]

BROCCOLI AND CABBAGE TOSS * * * * *

Cabbage (Chinese, Nappa or Savvoy)
Lettuce, preferably Romaine
Broccoli
Tomatoes
Turnips or kohlrabi
Alfalfa sprouts
Dulse (optional)

1. Wash and break up cabbage and lettuce and coarsely cut up broccoli.
2. Wash and cut up tomatoes.
3. Place these ingredients in a large bowl and peel and dice turnips or kohlrabi.
4. Place turnips (or kohlrabi) in the large bowl, along with alfalfa sprouts (and well-rinsed and chopped up dulse, if used).
5. Mix all ingredients together thoroughly and serve in salad bowls.
6. With nuts, seeds or avocados, this makes a complete meal.

EGGPLANT SALAD * * * *

For two servings:
1 eggplant
3-4 tomatoes
1 stalk celery
1 avocado (optional)
Lettuce or sprouts

1. Peel and dice eggplant into bite-sized chunks and place on a steamer in a pan with about 1-½ inches of water in it.
2. With the lid on, start it steaming on high heat. Then lower the heat very low and steam for about five minutes.
3. Remove the lid away from you and place steamed eggplant in a large bowl with washed and cut up tomatoes.
4. Wash and cut up broccoli and celery and mix with tomatoes and steamed eggplant chunks in a large bowl.
5. A diced avocado may be added to make this a main-course salad.
6. Serve on a beds of lettuce on plates or in bowls lined with lettuce or sprouts.

T. C.'S SUPER SALAD *****

This wholesome salad is a meal in itself.

For four large servings:

2-3 lbs. tomatoes
1 lb. cauliflower
4 med. or lg. avocados
 (or 1 lb. ground nuts or seeds)
4 stalks celery
4 lg. red or green bell peppers
 (preferably red)
2 lbs. bok choy stalks and greens

1. Wash and dice tomatoes; chop or dice cauliflower, including stalks and leaves; quarter, peel and dice avocados (or add ground nuts or seeds); and place all ingredients in a large salad bowl.
2. Wash and dice celery and bell peppers and wash and cut up bok choy stalks and greens.
3. Add these ingredients to salad bowl and mix all ingredients together.

This salad is very chewy. It can be changed in many ways to achieve different taste objectives. For instance, the juice of a fresh-squeezed grapefruit may be added. Chopped turnips, kohlrabi or broccoli substitute well for the cauliflower or may be used along with it. Instead of bok choy you may want to use lettuce, Chinese cabbage, kale, collards, cabbage or other greens.

ASPARAGUS SALAD ****

For two servings:

**2 lbs. fresh asparagus
(or substitute frozen)**
**4 oz. raw pumpkin seeds
(pepitas) (or substitute
chopped almonds)**
4 leaves Romaine lettuce
2 lg. or 4 sm. tomatoes
1 lg. or 2 sm. stalks bok choy
**1 grapefruit (optional, if
tomatoes aren't very tasty)**

1. Asparagus may be used either raw or cooked (or a combination of the two.) If you use it raw, use only the tasty tender tips (or as much of the asparagus stalk as you like raw—taste-test it).
2. If you use the asparagus cooked, cut off the very tough and discolored bottom ends of the stalks and steam the tender ends for 2-3 minutes, taking care not to overcook.
3. You may use the tender tips raw and then steam the more fibrous (but not tough) portions and use both in your salad.
4. Cut up asparagus and place in a large mixing bowl, along with pumpkin seeds (or chopped or slivered almonds).
5. Wash, dry and cut or break up Romaine lettuce into large bowl and wash and cut up tomatoes into bowl.
6. Wash celery and bok choy, dice coarsely, and add to bowl.
7. If your tomatoes are not very tasty, you may wish to halve and juice a grapefruit and add juice to your salad.
8. Mix well and then chop up a bit with a paring knife to further blend ingredients.

RICE SALAD ***

The three-star rating is because of the cooked ingredients, rice, and because of the soy sauce, a fermented product that contains salt. If you leave out the soy sauce, this is a four-star recipe.

Brown rice
Distilled water
Red cabbage
Celery
Sprouts (mung, lentil, alfalfa, sunflower)
Lettuce
Avocado (optional)
Soy sauce, (tamari, shoyu) (optional)

1. Using a pan with a tight-fitting lid, bring to a boil one part brown rice and two parts distilled water.
2. Turn your burner down to very low heat and cook for 35 to 40 minutes, until all or almost all the water has been absorbed by the rice.
3. Place cooked rice in a large bowl. (If you're using soy sauce— tamari is best—add a little and mix in well.)
4. Finely chop up red cabbage and washed celery and add to rice mixture.
5. Add sprouts (and avocado if you're using it).
6. Mix all ingredients together well.
7. About half the mixture should consist of fresh vegetables and half of rice (or use an even larger portion of vegetables for a more wholesome salad).
8 Serve in salad bowls or on plates on a bed of lettuce.

GARBANZO BEAN SALAD ****

Garbanzo bean sprouts (from about
 2 oz. dry beans per serving)
Fresh green peas, about
 4-6 oz. per serving
Carrots, about ½ c. or
 4-6 oz. per serving
Creamy avocados, about one per serving

1. Shell peas and place in a steaming rack, along with sprouted garbanzos.
2. Put about ½ inch of water in the bottom of a pan with a tight-fitting lid, and set steamer of peas and beans in pan.
3. Start on high heat, and when steam begins to escape between the lid and the pan, turn to the lowest heat possible.
4. When beans and peas are cooked, turn off the heat and remove the lid, opening it away from you and holding it over the pan. (This will allow the water inside the lid to drip into the pan, and the steam will escape behind the pan instead of in front in your face.)
6. Lift the steamer out of the pan with a utensil, and spread beans and peas on a plate to cool somewhat.
7. Wash and grate carrots (or put them through a Champion juicer or food processor).
8. Place grated carrots in a large bowl and halve and pit avocados.
9. Remove creamy avocado flesh with a teaspoon and place in bowl with carrots.
10. Add peas and beans and mix thoroughly.

This salad is hearty and delicious. Because beans are starchy, and starches are a poor combination with proteins (nuts, seeds, etc.) and acids (tomatoes, lemons, etc.), have this salad with other starches or, preferably, with nonstarchy vegetables.

ZUCCHINI SALAD * * *

For two servings:

Zucchini squashes, a steamer
  rack full when cubed
Celery, 4-5 stalks
Cabbage, broccoli or other similar
  vegetable(s) in season, a two-inch
  wedge of cabbage, a stalk of broccoli, and/or a
  comparable amount of other vegetable(s)
Avocados, two
Dulse (or kelp), to taste
Nature's Gourmet or other salt-free
  herbal seasoning (optional), to taste

1. Wash zucchini; cube into bite-sized chunks; and steam about 8-10 minutes, until done.
2. Meantime, wash two stalks celery and dice up somewhat finely.
3. Cut up cabbage, broccoli and/or other vegetable(s) finely and place cut-up vegetables in a large bowl.
4. Wash carrots and remaining celery and prepare for juicing.
5. Juice carrots and celery and pour into blender.
6. Halve and pit avocados and scoop creamy flesh into blender with a teaspoon.
7. Liquefy on high speed until creamy.
8. Rinse a handful or so of dulse under cold water to remove salt; add to blender; and blend again, along with Nature's Gourmet (or other salt-free herbal seasoning), if you use it.
9. Place steamed zucchini and blender ingredients in large bowl with the cut-up vegetables and mix well.
10. Serve as a meal in itself or alongside a plate of washed lettuce and/or other raw veggies.

T. C. FRY'S PEA SALAD SPECIAL ****

For two servings:
1-½ lbs. fresh or frozen peas
1 lg. rutabaga
3 med. red potatoes
5 leaves Chinese cabbage
½ lb. broccoli
2 avocados
1 red bell pepper

1. Peel rutabagas but not potatoes, and steam both vegetables for 20 minutes on low heat (after starting steam on high heat). (You may need to cut up rutabagas so they're the same size as the potatoes.)
2. Steam peas seven minutes on low heat.
3. Wash and cut up Chinese cabbage leaves; dice broccoli, leaving smaller flowerettes whole; quarter, peel and dice avocados; and wash and dice red bell pepper.
4. Cool steamed potatoes and rutabagas by setting pan in sink and filling with cold water; then dice and place in a large bowl, along with diced raw vegetables and avocados.
5. Mix ingredients together well and serve.

YAM-SPROUT SALAD SUPREME * * * *

Red Garnet yams
Alfalfa sprouts
Celery
Cabbage (optional)
Romaine lettuce leaves (optional)
Carrots
Avocados

1. Steam whole washed yams 15-20 minutes on low heat (after starting steam on high heat). (Or use yams raw, if you wish.)
2. Break up alfalfa sprouts into a large bowl; wash, cut leaves off of, and dice celery; and grate cabbage (if you're using it).
3. Cool yams by first setting the pan in the sink and running cold water into it and then setting yams on a cooling rack, plate or cutting board.
4. While yams are cooling, wash and prepare carrots for juicing; make carrot juice; and place juice in blender.
5. Quarter and peel avocados; place flesh in blender with carrot juice; and liquefy on high speed until thick and creamy, adding more carrot juice or avocado as needed.
6. Dice yams and add to salad bowl, along with blender contents; mix well; and serve in bowls, or on whole Romaine lettuce leaves as sandwiches.

"Finger Salads"

A "finger salad," as the name implies, is a salad you eat with your fingers. It is a plate, platter or tray of whole and/or sliced vegetables (or fruits) that are either eaten as is or, more commonly, dunked into a dip.

Finger salads are an excellent change from the cut-up salad routine, and they are quicker and easier to prepare. They may be a bit messier to eat than a cut-up salad, but napkins or towels solve that problem. (Cotton napkins or terry cloth or woven cotton waffle weave or herringbone towels are especially nice and substantial.)

In addition to the variety finger salads provide, and their ease of preparation, they inspire creativity—on the part of both the "chef" and the eaters. Each person comes up with his or her own way of eating. Served with sharp knives, cutting boards, plates, bowls, forks and spoons, finger salads may turn into cut-up salads or lettuce leaf sandwiches, or they may be eaten in any manner the eater comes up with in his or her imagination.

Since the eaters decide which foods and how much to eat, finger salads allow more flexibility for individuals. Eaters can eat more of their favorite food items and less (or none) of their least favorite. Children have more fun eating this way and can learn to prepare meals themselves.

Besides their creative and educational value and their flexibility, finger salads offer a greater variety of flavor combinations than cut-up salads. Each bite can be a different food combination. Or eaters can vary the *amounts* of the various ingredients used. For example, one bite can consist of just pecan and tomato; the next of pecan, tomato and lettuce dipped in lemon juice; the next of pecan, tomato and cucumber. Also, you can vary the ratio of pecans to tomato to suit your own taste, experimenting with each bite until you discover the ratio you like best. Likewise, you can vary the amounts of other foods in your finger salad to obtain a variety of flavor combinations at a meal.

Of course cut-up salads have their advantages, too. For one, they provide an interesting, often exciting, blend of flavors. In addition, they can be eaten in bowls with forks or spoons. They are easy to eat and not messy. But cut-up salads do take a little time to prepare. Also, some nutrients are lost because oxidation occurs wherever the food is cut. As mentioned earlier, with cut-up salads you have just one basic combination flavor.

So, for variety, fun, education, ease of preparation, less oxidation and more nutrients, try finger salads!

SENSATIONAL SALAD DRESSINGS AND DIPS

There's nothing like a terrific salad dressing to make a salad taste out-of-this-world good! Likewise, salad dips transform whole or sliced vegetables from mediocre to simply tantalizing. And flavor isn't the only benefit from using salad dressings. The oils used in salad dressings and dips also provide a satiety that changes a salad (or uncut vegetables) from a (too-light) side dish into a nutritious and satisfying main course.

Traditional salad dressings are made with free vegetable oils. These, including the "cold-pressed" versions, are not healthful because oils quickly lose their freshness and, consequently, their wholesomeness once they're separated from their whole food sources. The healthful natural sources of unfragmented oils are nuts, seeds and avocados. Thus these comprise the base of most dips and dressings for vegetables and vegetable salads. (Since nuts and seeds are rich in protein, as well as natural oils, dressings containing them are *not* recommended on salads containing starches [rice, potatoes, yams, etc.], since starches tend to ferment rather than being efficiently digested when eaten with high-protein foods. Low-protein avocado-based dressings are better with starchy foods.)

A second basic ingredient in vegetable salads is an acid. Vinegar is usually used but, like free oils, it is unwholesome. Vinegar (acetic acid) is a fermented product that irritates body cells and tissues. Instead of it, I recommend lemon, lime or grapefruit juice and/or tomatoes as acids. Or, particularly when your salad or meal contains potatoes or other starchy food, you may use a salad dressing without an acid. (Acids inhibit starch digestion.)

The final basic ingredient of salad dressings and dips is seasonings. The salt and other seasonings used in traditional salad dressings is harmful and irritating to the body; but the nuts, seeds, avocados, and acid fruits used in the recipes given here are so tasty that seasonings are not required. However, for added flavor and particularly snazzy dressings, some of the recipes call for nonirritating whole food seasonings such as fresh celery, parsley or other aromatic vegetables. People not yet willing to entirely abandon seasonings may use the salt-free herbal seasonings or dulse, kelp or other seaweeds for a stronger flavor (though these can

41

and do at least somewhat interfere with digestion, as do all seasonings).

The following sample salad dressing and dip recipes will get you started on the right track; then *you* can take it from there!

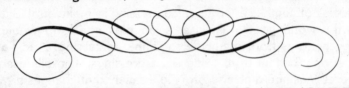

GARBANZO BEAN DRESSING/DIP/SPREAD [HOMMUS] * * *

8 oz. sprouted garbanzos
2 oz. Brazil nuts
1 sm. or ½ lg. lemon or lime, juiced
1 stalk celery, juiced
Dr. Bonner's Balanced Mineral Seasoning,
  Bernard Jenson's Quick-Sip "Bouillon
  Concentrate," and/or other tasty
  vegetable seasoning(s)

1. Alternately put sprouted garbanzos and Brazil nuts through Champion juicer (with juicer blank in place).
2. Add and stir in lemon or lime juice, celery juice, and seasonings to taste. (If you wish, you may liquefy diced celery in lemon or lime juice instead of juicing it in a juicer.)
3. Whether this is a dressing, a dip or a spread depends upon how much liquid you use in proportion to the beans and nuts.

ZESTY GUACAMOLE DRESSING/DIP ****

For 1-2 servings:
1 lg. or 2 sm. soft avocado(s)
1 lime or lemon
2 tomatillos (optional)
Dr. Bronner's Balanced Mineral Seasoning
Bernard Jenson's Quick-Sip "Boullion Concentrate"

1. Quarter avocado; remove pit; peel (by hand); and place flesh on a plate.
2. Mash avocado with a fork, and, using a rubber spatula, transfer mashed avocado into a bowl.
3. Juice lime or lemon.
4. If you have tomatillos, remove husks; wash and quarter tomatillos; place in blender with lime or lemon juice; and liquefy on high speed.
5. Pour citrus juice (or citrus juice and tomatillo mixture) into bowl of mashed avocado.
6. Add Dr. Bronner's Balanced Mineral Seasoning and Bernard Jenson's Quick-Sip and stir all ingredients together.
7. Taste and add more seasonings as needed—until it tastes WILD!
8. Use as a dip for red bell pepper slices, celery stalks, peeled cucumber slices, washed lettuce leaves, broccoli stalks and flowerettes, cauliflower, etc., or as a delightfully-delicious dressing for your favorite salad.

Note: Use as soon as possible after making, since mashed avocados don't store well.

SUPERCADO DRESSING/DIP *****

For two servings:
½ lemon
1 med. tomato
2 stalks celery
1 med. avocado

1. Juice lemon half and pour juice into blender.
2. Wash and quarter tomato; add to blender; and liquefy with lemon juice on highest blender speed.
3. Wash celery; cut off leaves; and cut into fourths.
4. Turn blender on highest speed; remove centerpiece from lid; and add celery, one piece at a time. Stop and stir if/when necessary.
5. Slice avocado in half and remove pit. Scoop flesh with spoon into blender until well blended.
6. Use as a very versatile dressing for any salad, or as a dip for your favorite veggies in season!

Note: Use as soon as possible after making, since mashed or blended avocados don't store well.

PIGNOLIA DRESSING OR DIP *****

Tomatoes
Tomatillos (or lemon
 or lime juice) (optional)
Pignolia nuts

1. Wash and quarter tomatoes; place in blender; and liquefy on high speed.
2. Remove coverings from tomatillos; wash and quarter tomatillos; and add to blended tomatoes. (Or add juice from lemon or lime, a little at a time, taking care not to add too much—taste as you add.)
3. Blend on high speed until tomatillos are liquefied.
4. With blender running, gradually add pignolias until mixture becomes thick, stopping and stirring as needed.
5. Serve over a vegetable salad or place in bowl or cups to use as a dip.

SEASONED CARROT-AVOCADO DRESSING OR DIP

For two large servings:
6-8 carrots, preferably organic
4-5 stalks celery
2 avocados
Dulse or kelp, to taste
Nature's Gourmet or other salt-free
  herbal seasoning, to taste

1. Wash and juice carrots and celery, and pour juice into blender.
2. Quarter, pit and peel avocados; add to blender; and liquefy until creamy.
3. Wash dulse (if you're using it) under cold water to remove salt; place it and/or kelp in blender, along with Nature's Gourmet (or other salt-free herbal seasoning); and blend again.
4. Pour over salad of your choice and mix well; pour on top of individual salads; or use as a dip for raw vegetables and lettuce leaves.

SWEET ALMOND DRESSING OR DIP *****

Almonds
Carrot juice

1. Grind almonds in a nut and seed grinder or in your blender.
2. Place ground almonds and carrot juice in blender and liquefy on high speed until well blended, adding more juice or ground almonds until desired consistency is obtained.

SUPER PECAN DRESSING OR DIP ****

For two servings:

**3-4 tomatillos (or juice or a
  sm. lemon or lime)**
Grapefruit, juiced
**½ pt. cherry tomatoes (or
  2 regular tomatoes)**
4-5 stalks celery
6 oz. shelled pecans

1. Remove husks from tomatillos; wash and quarter tomatillos; and place in blender. (Or place lemon or lime juice in blender.)
2. Add grapefruit juice to blender, along with washed cherry tomatoes or washed and quartered regular tomatoes.
3. Liquefy blender ingredients on high speed; then wash celery, cut off leaves, and cut stalks into sixths.
4. While blender is running, add celery through opening in blender lid and continue blending until liquefied, turning blender off and on as needed.
5. Taste. If mixture is too sweet, too acid, or not tasty enough, add more celery and taste again.
6. When blender mixture tastes great, turn on blender and gradually add pecans through opening in blender lid, stopping and stirring as often as necessary.
7. Add more tomatoes or pecans as needed to make mixture thin or thick enough. (I usually make this dressing/dip quite thick.)

This is one of the most delicious if not *the* most delicious, dressings ever! Try it and see!

CAPTIVATING CAKES

Baked concoctions such as cookies, cakes, breads, pies, etc., are generally unhealthful on many counts. They usually contain an incompatible digestive combination of starch (flour) with sugar or honey. Plus they have other unwholesome ingredients including salt, baking soda, eggs, milk, yeast, shortening, and so on.

Since baked pastries, cake, cookies, etc., contain such unwholesome ingredients that also do not digest well together, you will feel much better and get sick far less if you discontinue eating these foods. If you have a birthday or other special celebration, you can serve fruits, fruit salads, dates, dried figs, fresh juices and smoothies, and other delicious and elegant wholesome foods.

Either in addition to, or instead or these ideally wholesome foods, you can make relatively healthful unbaked cakes. The three sample recipes given here use the incompatible digestive combination of fruits and nuts together (which gives them four-star ratings); but they are minus flour, eggs, milk, baking soda, shortening, and the other unwholesome ingredients used in conventional cakes. To this extent, and because they are not baked, the cake recipes given here are more wholesome than the traditional baked cakes.

PARADISE CAKE ****

This is an unbaked cake of all uncooked ingredients. Though absolutely delightful in flavor and texture, it does consist of an incompatible digestive combination—nuts and coconut with sweet fruits. This accounts for the four-star rating.

For one lg. or two sm. cakes:

**1 lb. coconut meal, unsweetened (shredded
   may be used if meal is unavailable)**
1 lb. nuts (pecans, almonds or walnuts)
**12 oz. soaked dried fruit (figs,
   raisins) and/or dates**
8-10 med. bananas
**Fresh fruit (plums, peaches, apples,
   pears, pineapple, strawberries, etc.)**

1. Liquefy soaked dried fruit (and/or dates) on highest blender speed, using soak water (and/or distilled water) as needed.
2. Grind nuts (and coconut, if shredded and not a meal) in a nut and seed grinder or blender.
3. Place nuts and coconut in a large mixing bowl; add blended fruit mixture; and mix well, using your hands rather than a spoon. At this point the mixture should be moist but hold together. Add more nuts/coconut or water if needed.
4. Slice bananas and selected fresh fruit into bite-size pieces; add to mixture; and mix in with your hands.
5. Place mixture evenly in one large rectangular or two small square cake pans and sprinkle coconut on top.
6. Place cake in freezer for several hours or overnight. When cake is just barely frozen but firm, it's ready to eat. (If the cake is frozen solid, let it partially thaw 1-3 hours or so before serving.)

STRAWBERRY SHORTCAKE ****

Almonds
Distilled water
Fresh strawberries

1. Grind almonds in a nut grinder or blender; pour almond meal into a bowl; and add just enough distilled water to moisten.
2. Mix well and spread a very thin layer of almond "crust" in a bowl. (A thin layer is recommended because this "crust" is quite rich.)
3. Remove stems, wash, and cut up strawberries until they become juicy. Use a fork to mash them a little if necessary.
4. Pour lots of strawberries over almond "biscuits" and serve.

If you want milk or cream on top, make wholesome nondairy almond milk or almond cream:

a. Blanch almonds in hot or boiling water to pinch off skins.
b. Blend one part blanched almonds with four parts distilled water for nut milk, or blend equal parts almonds and water to make nut cream. [Water and nut amounts can be adjusted to your taste.]
c. Pour nut milk or cream over strawberry shortcake.

It is preferable to eat this dish alone. If you eat anything else at the same meal, let it be other berries or citrus and/or nuts or seeds. Lettuce or celery also combine fairly well with Strawberry Shortcake.

PINEAPPLE SHORTCAKE * * * *

Walnuts
Distilled water
Fresh pineapple
Milk from a fresh coconut (optional)

1. Grind up walnuts in a nut grinder or blender and pour into a bowl.
2. Add just enough distilled water to moisten walnut meal and mix well.
3. Pat walnut mixture into bottom of serving bowls in a thin "crust."
4. Cut rosette of spiked leaves off top of pineapple; quarter pineapple lengthwise; and slice off cores.
5. Undercut each quarter with the tip of a sharp knife; cut one vertical slice down the center of each quarter; and cut several ¾-inch horizontal slices.
6. Place pineapple chunks in a bowl and, with the tip of a teaspoon, scrape pineapple from husks into bowl.
7. Cut up pineapple very finely and pour lots of it over walnut "crust."
8. If you wish, you may serve coconut milk on top of Pineapple Shortcake:
   a. Make two holes in the eyes of a coconut and pour milk into a glass or other container with a double cheesecloth rubber-banded over the top to catch the fiber and debris.
   b. To make a richer milk, blend some coconut meat with the coconut milk. [The more meat you use, the richer the milk will be.]
   c. Pour desired amount of coconut milk over Pineapple Short-cake.
9. Serve alone (preferably), or with other nuts or acid fruits.

ENTICING CANDIES

Everybody knows that candy, though it tastes good, isn't really good for us—that is, *most candy* isn't healthful. Just as with other kinds of foods, however, there are healthier versions of candy, too.

Ideally, candies should be made with ingredients that are natually sweet—dried fruits for example. Or, they should be sweetened with dates or dried fruits, since these are the only healthful sweeteners. Date sugar and malt syrup (barley malt) are not particularly healthful, but they are better than refined sugars and honeys.

While natural candies can be habit-forming, you will feel best and get sick least if you make them an occasional treat and get in the habit of eating fresh fruits, dates, and dried fruits as your sweets.

WANDA'S ORANGE-ALMOND CANDY *

¼ c. malt syrup
Few drops orange extract
Grated organic orange rind (optional)
Appr. ½ c. raw almond butter

1. Combine all ingredients to make a stiff mixture.
2. Spoon onto a cookie sheet lined with waxed paper and freeze.

WANDA'S TAHINI CANDY **

¼ c. malt syrup
¼-½ c. date sugar
Appr. ½ c. raw sesame tahini

1. Combine ingredients to make a stiff mixture.
2. Pat into a waxed paper-lined pan; cut into squares; and freeze until firm.

CAROB-COCONUT BALLS * * *

Shredded coconut
Carob powder, preferably unroasted
Distilled water
Lecithin (liquid form)

1. Pour carob powder into mixing bowl; add very small amount of distilled water; and mix.
2. Add just a little more distilled water and continue mixing.
3. Continue adding very small amounts of water and mixing until a smooth, creamy consistency is obtained.
4. Add coconut and mix in.
5. Continue adding coconut until you have to mix with your hands; then add about one to two teaspoons of liquid lecithin and mix in thoroughly, using your hands and kneading the mixture.
6. Additional coconut may be added if more stiffness is desired; more lecithin may be added if mixture does not stick together well at this point.
7. Roll into small balls and roll each ball in coconut.
8. Place balls in a plate or in a covered container for easy storage, and store in refrigerator.

CAROB-COCONUT-ALMOND BALLS * * *

Follow recipe for Carob-Coconut Balls and add chopped almonds at the same time as the coconut.

DIVINE DRINKS

What comes to mind when you think of drinks or beverages? Alcoholic beverages? Cokes or other soft drinks? Coffee, tea or hot chocolate? Lemonade? Iced tea? These are some of the most commonly-used drinks, unfortunately. Unfortunately because all are unhealthful and contribute to unnecessary sicknesses, diseases, and suffering. If we didn't drink so many caffeine- and sugar-loaded beverages, we'd be a whole lot better off healthwise.

Caffeine and sugar may temporarily give the *illusion* of energy, but their long-run effect is a drain on the body's supply of nerve energy. In short, you wear your body out when you constantly stimulate and goad it with drug-substances.

In addition to the toxic nature of the drinks commonly consumed, much drinking is done at or with meals. This is a bad habit because liquids (even water) taken with a meal dilute the digestive juices and interfere with digestion. When digestion does not progress efficiently, bacteria decompose foods, and the toxic by-products of decomposition add to the body's toxic load that makes us sick and lethargic.

Tools for creating divine drinks!

What and how do we drink, then, so as to be healthy and energetic, free from toxins, sicknesses, and diseases? You can drink delicious, easy-to-prepare fruit juices, blends and smoothies; vegetable juices and blends; and nuts and seed "milks." These wholesome drinks can be used as meals or drank one-half hour to one hour before a meal. In this manner, they do not interfere with digestion.

When you try out the sample drink recipes given here, you will probably be surprised how delicious they are. And no doubt you will come up with many of your own creations. (For more delightful drink recipes, order Marti Wheeler Fry's new recipe book, *Delectable All-Raw Juices, Blends and Smoothies.*)

WORLD'S BEST FRUIT BLEND *****

For one lg. serving:
3 Red Delicious apples
1 Gravenstein or other tart apple
1 ripe med.-lg. persimmon

1. Wash apples; halve; remove stems; and cut into eighths.
2. Put apples through juicer; then pour apple juice into blender.
3. De-stem persimmon and add to blender.
4. Liquefy on high speed until well blended and serve.

VICKI'S SENSATIONAL BERRY JULIP ****

Fresh blackberries (and/or other
  berries of your choice)
Sweet grapes or apples
Peppermint or other mint tea

1. Wash berries; place in blender; add juice of sweet grapes or apples (to sweeten); and liquefy on high speed until well blended.
2. Using three parts berry blend to one part peppermint or other mint tea, add tea to blender and blend again.
3. Serve. If you wish, you may garnish with a sprig of peppermint and/or one or more berries floating on top.

CAROB-COCONUT SMOOTHIE ***

1 c. distilled water
¼ c. unsweetened coconut
2 t. carob powder
1-½ fresh or frozen bananas

1. Place water, coconut and carob powder in blender and liquefy on high speed.
2. With blender running, add bananas, one-half banana at a time, through opening in blender lid and continue liquefying until well blended. (Frozen bananas make this drink much thicker and colder than fresh bananas.)
3. Serve as a meal in itself.

SPICED CAROB-ALMOND SMOOTHIE **

Almonds
Distilled water
Carob powder, preferably unroasted
Bananas
Vanilla
Cinnamon

1. Peel very ripe bananas, place in plastic bags and freeze, preferably overnight.
2. Blanch almonds by pouring boiling or very hot water over them and then pinching off their skins between your thumb and your fingers.
3. Discard skins and blend about one part blanched almonds with three parts distilled water, using highest blender speed. (The proportion of almonds to water can be adjusted according to the degree of richness you desire.)
4. Blend frozen bananas into almond "milk," again blending at high speed.
5. Add vanilla and cinnamon to taste, along with about one or two teaspoons carob powder per serving.
6. Blend again; then, with blender still running, add more frozen bananas through opening in blender lid, one-half banana at a time, until desired thickness is obtained.
7. Serve freshly-made in chilled glasses.
   This is a meal in itself!

MELON CREAMY *****

Ripe melon(s) of your choice (Honeydew, Scharlyn, cantaloupe, Persian melon)

1. Set melon on cutting board in horizontal position; cut in half vertically (so juice and seeds don't spill onto cutting board and countertop); lift off top half of melon; and scoop seeds into a bowl.
2. Slice each half vertically into six to eight 1-½" to 2" strips.
3. Holding each slice in your hand and using a sharp knife, peel off rind.
4. Place peeled melon slices side by side on cutting board; if melons are medium or large, cut strips horizontally into halves or thirds; place 1-3 melon pieces in blender; and liquefy on high speed.
5. Remove centerpiece from blender lid and, with blender running on high speed, add remaining melon pieces, one or two at a time.
6. Continue blending for another couple minutes to make a very smooth, creamy drink.

PERKY PINEAPPLE BLEND *****

1 part fresh pineapple
2 parts red grapes
1 part oranges

1. Place prepared pineapple in blender.
2. Make grape juice in a regular juicer and orange juice in a citrus juicer.
3. Add grape juice and orange juice to blender and liquefy a few minutes on high speed, until smooth.

SMILE-INDUCING BIG PINK JUICE * * * * *

For two glasses:
¼ ripe Hawaiian pineapple
1 pint strawberries
1 Red Delicious apple
1 Pippin or other tart apple

1. Cut top off pineapple; quarter and core; undercut pineapple from rind; and, leaving pineapple on rind, cut into 6-8 large chunks.
2. Place pineapple chunks in blender, along with pineapple you can scrape from husks with a spoon.
3. De-stem and wash strawberries.
4. Wash apples and cut into juicer-sized slices, discarding only the stem. (The core and seeds can be handled by the juicer.)
5. Put apples through juicer; pour apple juice into blender; and liquefy with pineapple a couple minutes on high speed.
6. With the blender still running, remove centerpiece from blender lid and add strawberries, a few at a time.
7. Continue blending a minute or so; then pour and enjoy!

LIP-SMACKIN' DATE SMOOTHIE * * * * *

Fresh fruit juice
Dates, 2-4 per serving
Frozen bananas

1. Use freshly-made apple, grape or pear juice as a base.
2. Place juice in blender; pit dates; add pitted dates to juice; and blend at high speed. (Dried apples may also be used and added at this time.)
3. Add frozen bananas, one-half banana at a time, through opening in blender lid while blender is running on high speed. (A relatively small amount of fresh ripe bananas may also be used if desired.)

This creamy-smooth drink is a meal in itself. Lip-smackin' good!

STRIKING BROCCOLI-CARROT BLEND * * * * *

1 part broccoli
3 parts carrots

1. Prepare carrots for juicing and put through juicer.
2. Wash broccoli; cut to fit through juicer mouth; and juice.
3. Stir or blend the two juices together and serve.

Unusually delicious (when vegetables used are high quality) and extremely nutritious!

LIMEY CELERY-TOMATO BLEND * * * * *

1 part celery
1 part tomatoes
Lime, about 1/8-1/4 per serving

1. Wash celery and tomatoes; cut celery to fit through juicer mouth; and quarter tomatoes.
2. Juice celery in juicer and liquefy tomatoes in blender.
3. Pour celery juice into blender; add lime juice to taste; blend again; and serve.

APPLE CIDER * * * * *

8 parts apples
4 parts celery
1 part lemon

1. Wash apples and celery.
2. Remove stems from apples and cut leaves off celery.
3. Cut up apples and celery as needed to fit through juicer mouth and juice.
4. Halve and juice lemon.
5. Stir or blend juices together and serve.
   Really good!

SATISFYING ALMOND NUT MILK * * * * *

1 part almonds
8 parts distilled water

1. For a creamy white nut milk, blanch almonds by pouring very hot (almost boiling) water over them to loosen skins.
2. Remove skins by pinching each almond between your thumb and index finger.
3. Place almonds in one bowl and skins in another.
4. Blend blanched almonds with distilled water, using highest blender speed for three minutes.

Delightful!

   a. If you choose not to blanch almonds, use them whole or grind them in a nut-and-seed grinder or food mill.
   b. Blend almonds (or almond meal) on high speed with water.

Almond nut milk made this way is not as white or as creamy as almond milk made with blanched almonds, but it is equally as delicious, as well as easy.

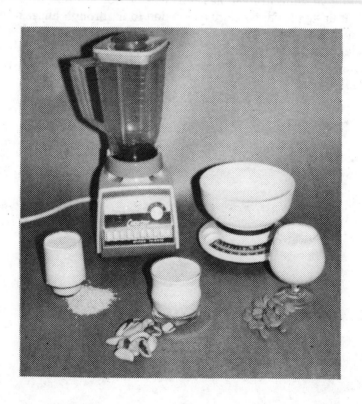

FANTASTIC FRUIT SAUCES

Applesauce is the sauce most people are familiar with. But why limit fruit sauces to apples only? There are several kinds of luscious fruits that can be made into wonderful sauces.

Fruit sauces can be used in a variety of ways. They can be eaten as is with fresh and/or dried fruits; or they can be eaten as a thick fruit soup with one or more kinds of cut-up fresh and/or dried fruits mixed in. In addition, fruit sauces can be used as dressings for fruit salads, as dips for fruit slices or bananas, or as spreads for fruit "sandwiches." Fruit sauces also make excellent toppings for All-Natural Banana Ice Cream.

The following recipes may well make you a fruit sauce fan. Why not try some of them out and see?

EASY-AS-PIE APPLESAUCE * * * * *

Apples

1. If you have a Champion juicer, peel and core apples; put them through the juicer (with the blank in place); and serve immediately.
2. If you have an Acme juicer but no Champion, peel and core apples; put them through the juicer, making juice; and then remove the pulp from the basket and, in a bowl, mix the juice with the pulp.
3. If you have a blender but no juicer, peel, core and dice apples and blend them with a little distilled water, stopping, pressing apples against blender blades, and restarting as needed.

APRISAUCE *****

Apples
Dried apricots
Dates (optional)

1. Soak dried apricots overnight or several hours in distilled water.
2. Wash, quarter, core and dice apples. (A mixture of some tart apples and some sweet apples gives zest.)
3. Juice some of the apples in an Acme or Champion juicer and pour juice into blender, along with soak water from apricots.
4. Pit a few dates; add to blender with a few soaked apricots; and blend at high speed.
5. With blender running on high speed, remove opening in lid and gradually add diced apples and soaked apricots, blending until desired consistency is obtained.
6. If you need more liquid, make and add some more apple juice or use distilled water.

Aprisauce is even tastier than plain applesauce!

Note: If you don't have a juicer or prefer not to use one, you may substitute distilled water for the apple juice. It is also possible to make Aprisauce without soaking the dried apricots if you're making this dish at the last minute.

PINEAPPLE SAUCE ****

Dried pineapple
Distilled water
Fresh pineapple (optional)

1. Place dried pineapples (preferably not sugar- or honey-dipped) in a small bowl or covered dish.
2. Add enough distilled water to cover and allow to soak several hours or (preferably) overnight.
3. Place both the soaked pineapples and their soak water in blender and liquefy on high speed. (The texture will be very similar to applesauce.)
4. If you wish, you may prepare a fresh pineapple and add the sweet part of it to the blender before liquefying.

PEARSAUCE *****

Fresh and/or dried pears
Distilled water
Dates (optional)

1. Quarter and core fresh pears and/or soak dried pears overnight or several hours in enough distilled water to cover them.
2. Using just enough distilled water and/or soak water to blend, liquefy ingredients on highest blender speed. The mixture will become creamy in texture.
3. Dried pears provide enough sweetness, but if you desire more sweetness, or if you use fresh pears only, you may want to pit a few dates and blend them with your mixture.

Better than applesauce, Pearsauce is delicious with ripe bananas sliced up on top or mixed in.

SUPER-DELICIOUS NATURAL ICE CREAMS

Old-fashioned homemade ice creams (and the first factory-made ice creams) contained only fresh milk and cream, sugar, eggs, and natural flavorings. But these ingredients are unhealthful. Milk is a food only for babies under age three (and then only from their mothers); sugar is notoriously unhealthful; and eggs are inherently unwholesome, not to mention how laying chickens are housed in ridiculously crowded conditions and stimulated by drugs and horrendous conditions to overproduce.

But to make matters worse yet, most of today's ice creams contain such ingredients as milk fat and nonfat milk, sugar, corn sweetener, whey, mono- and diglycerides, guar gum, Polysorbate 80, carrageenin, and natural and artificial flavorings. Ice cream has gone from bad to worse.

With this information in hand, who would dare say that ice cream can be healthful? Sure, there are ice creams made with honey or date sugar instead of white sugar; ice creams made without harmful chemicals used as stablizers, emulsifiers and flavorings; and even ice creams made with soybeans instead of cow's milk. But since honey, date sugar, soybeans, natural flavorings, and the salt used in ice creams are unwholesome, too, what hope could there be for this delicious frozen treat that everyone loves so?

Take heart! There *is* hope! Ice cream can be made from completely healthful food—and still taste fabulous. In fact, making super-delicious, creamy, downright *wholesome* ice cream requires very little—frozen bananas and a Champion juicer. The result of feeding frozen ripe bananas through a Champion juicer is the most incredible frozen delight you'll ever want to taste! Check out the following super-delicious natural ice cream recipes, and see if you don't thoroughly agree!

ALL-NATURAL BANANA ICE CREAM * * * * *

Ripe bananas

1. Peel ripe bananas; place in a single layer in plastic bags; secure with twisties; and freeze overnight (or several hours).
2. At least 15 minutes before making All-Natural Banana Ice Cream, assemble juicer parts so the blank (not the screen) is in place, and put assembled parts and juicer blade in freezer. (This is so the first banana you put through the juicer won't come out melted.)
3. Make All-Natural Banana Ice Cream *immediately* before eating it. (Do not store in freezer.) Put juicer blade and attachment on juicer and place a bowl at end of attachment.
4. Remove frozen bananas from freezer; break bananas in half; and feed through juicer. Out comes a rich, creamy frozen custard!

This frozen delight is superb! It's great in hot weather and for special occasions; it makes a meal in itself; and it's very nutritious.

STRAWBERRY-BANANA ICE CREAM * * * * *

Frozen bananas
Fresh strawberries

1. Make this delightful frozen treat the same way as All-Natural Banana Ice Cream (see recipe) with one exception:
2. Wash, de-stem and freeze the best fresh strawberries you can find.
3. Put three or four frozen strawberries into Champion juicer mouth along with each frozen banana half. Out comes a fantastic pink frozen custard!

BAN-APPLE ICE CREAM SUPREME *****

Frozen bananas
Dried apples
Fresh bananas
Fresh apples (optional)
Fresh grapes (optional)

1. Assemble Champion juicer parts with the blank in place and place in freezer, along with juicer blade, for at least 10 minutes.
2. Wash fresh apples, if you use them (peel if not organically grown) and dice into large bowl.
3. If you use grapes, wash them and remove from stems. Halve and de-seed grapes if you are not using a seedless variety.
4. Peel and slice up bananas; and toss fresh fruits together.
5. If needed, put a little Crisco on the connection point of the juicer itself and slip on the blade.
6. Add juicer attachment and feed frozen bananas and dried apples through alternately, using bananas to push dried apples through.
7. Serve in bowls with the fresh fruit on top (or on the bottom).
8. Serve immediately, with or without a fruit salad topping or fruit sauce.

COOL CAROB SUNDAE *****

Distilled water, dried fruit or raisin soak
water, and/or freshly-made fruit juice
Dates, preferably soft ones
Carob powder, preferably unroasted
All-Natural Banana Ice Cream,
Strawberry-Banana Ice cream, and/or
Ban-Apple Ice Cream (see recipes)

1. Pour liquid(s) of your choice into blender; then pit and add several (soft) dates and liquefy them in liquid until well blended.
2. Carefully add carob powder and blend in, stopping blender to stir or add more carob powder or liquid as needed and then replacing blender lid and blending again.
3. Carob syrup should be medium-thick (not watery) and smooth. Use a narrow plastic spatula to get most of the syrup into a bowl or other container. (You can make a surplus and store it in your refrigerator. If you do this, you may want to pour carob syrup into a storage container with a tight-fitting lid.)
4. Make ice cream and scoop carob syrup on top. If you soaked raisins beforehand, you may wish to sprinkle some on top; or use unsoaked raisins.

   This makes a smashing wholesome meal!

NUTRITIOUS BANANA SPLIT ★ ★ ★ ★

Fresh bananas
Carob syrup (see Cool Carob
  Sundae recipe)
All-Natural Banana Ice Cream,
  Strawberry-Banana Ice Cream,
  and/or Ban-Apple Ice Cream (see recipes)
Grated unsweetened coconut (optional)

1. Slice fresh bananas into bowl and make carob syrup.
2. Make ice cream(s); place in bowls with fresh bananas; add carob syrup and coconut (if you're using it); and serve.

  An unusually-delicious treat, this makes a wonderful lunch meal for a hot summer day.

PINEAPPLE SHERBET ★ ★ ★ ★ ★

Pineapple, fresh and removed from husk
Fresh strawberries, washed,
  de-stemmed and sliced
Fresh mint sprig (optional)

1. Blend pineapple until smooth and pour into a freezer container.
2. Freeze until semi-hard and then stir well and fold in sliced strawberries.
3. Freeze overnight.
4. Serve with a single sprig of fresh mint as a garnish on each dish.

MOUTH-WATERING MAIN DISHES

Main-course salads are staples in a healthful diet, but not all wholesome main dishes have to be salads. The following Mouth-Watering Main Dishes are more healthful versions of some of the foods you may be accustomed to eating.

The factors that make the following recipes more nourishing and less toxic (thus more wholesome) than traditional main-dish recipes are many. Some of these factors include: more uncooked ingredients; few, if any, toxin-containing ingredients; no cheese or other dairy foods; few, if any, condiments; no animal fats, if any, incompatible digestive combinations, such as protein-starch combinations, as in pastas.

When you try out the recipes in this section, I'm sure you will be pleased. And perhaps you will come up with many ideas of your own, too!

◆

SEASONED POTATOES WITH "NATURE'S BUTTER" * * *

Potatoes, preferably organic
Avocados
Nature's Gourmet, Bernard Jensen's
  Organic Seasoning and Instant
  Gravy, and/or other salt-free
  herbal seasoning
Powdered kelp

1. Steam washed whole medium-small potatoes for 20 minutes.
2. Slice steamed potatoes about ¾" thick in lengthwise slices and lay on plates.
3. Quarter peel and mash avocados and use as "natures butter."
4. Season lightly with Nature's Gourmet, Bernard Jensen's Organic Seasoning and Instant Gravy (especially tasty); and/or other salt-free herbal seasoning, and more heavily with powdered kelp.

Eat alongside a large plate of washed Romaine or other lettuce and/or a large salad, preferably containing no acids (tomatoes, lemon juice, grapefruit juice, etc.) or proteins (nuts, seeds, etc.).

BAKED FRENCH FRIES ****

Potatoes, preferably organic

1. Preheat oven to 450 degrees.
2. Steam washed whole potatoes until just done (15-20 minutes for medium-small potatoes); slice in half lengthwise; and allow to cool on a plate, cutting board or rack.
3. Slice potatoes into desired size and shape, place on a cookie sheet and bake until crispy.

CORN CASSEROLE ****

Sweet corn
Avocados
Turnips
Celery
Sprouts (optional)
Lettuce (optional)

1. Husk corn and steam on a steamer rack in a large pan with about an inch of water in the bottom. Cover pan with a tight-fitting lid and bring to a steam on high heat. Then turn the temperature low and steam about eight minutes. (Or steam frozen corn, if fresh is not available.)
2. When corn is finished steaming, open the pan away from you and place steamed ears on a flat surface (cooling racks if you have them). (If the ears do not touch each other, they will cool more quickly.)
3. Quarter and peel avocados; peel turnips; and slice turnips to fit through the mouth of a Champion juicer.
4. With the juicer blank in place, put the avocados and then the turnips through the juicer into a bowl and stir together.
5. Cut corn off cooled ears into a large bowl, scraping the ears with a sharp knife to get all the corn off.
6. Wash and dice celery (about one stalk per person) and add to corn.
7. Add avocado and turnip mixture and mix thoroughly.

   This casserole is very chewy and delicious and may be served a variety of ways: on a thick bed of sprouts, on washed whole (Romaine) lettuce leaves as "tacos," in a large bowl with or without lots of sprouts on top (or mixed in), etc. Use your imagination!

VEGETARIAN SLOPPY JOES

Traditional Version * * *

Corn tortillas, steamed
Assorted greens/veggies, cut up
Cut-up cilantro (optional)
Ground sesame seeds mixed with
  a little hot sauce

1. Mix together all ingredients except tortillas.
2. Place mixture on tortillas, roll up, and eat!

Hygienic Version * * * * *

Washed whole Romaine lettuce leaves
Assorted greens/veggies, cut up
Ground sesame seeds
Tomatoes
Celery
Lemon, lime and/or grapefruit juice
Cilantro (optional)
Avocado(s)

1. Wash and liquefy tomatoes on high blender speed; and add small amount of lemon, lime and/or grapefruit juice.
2. Wash celery; cut off leaves; and cut stalks into sixths.
3. With blender running on high speed, gradually add celery (and washed cilantro if you're using it).
4. Stop blender and taste mixture. If it tastes too acid or bland, prepare and blend in more celery, until it tastes terrific.
5. Quarter, peel and add avocado(s) to thicken, and blend until smooth.
6. In a large bowl, mix together cut-up greens and veggies, ground sesame seeds, and avocado-celery-tomato mixture and mix well.
7. Serve spread down the center of washed whole lettuce leaves, fold or roll up, and eat, sandwich-style, with your hands.

EGGPLANT PARMIGIANA ***

For two servings:
2 med. eggplants
8 oz. cashews
3 med. tomatoes
2 stalks celery
1 red (or green) bell pepper

1. Peel eggplants, slice ¾" thick, and steam 6-8 minutes on low heat (after bringing to a steam on high heat).
2. Grind cashews in a blender or nut and seed grinder; place in a bowl; and set aside.
3. Make fresh tomato sauce (see recipe below); slice tomatoes (circular slices); and dice celery and pepper.
4. Place steamed eggplant slices on serving plates and layer on sliced tomatoes, diced celery and pepper, and ground cashews.
5. Add another layer of sliced and diced veggies and ground cashews and serve.

Fresh Tomato Sauce ****

5 med. tomatoes
½ lemon or lime, juiced
4-6 stalks celery
Nature's Gourmet or other salt-free
  vegetable seasoning, Dr. Bronner's
  Balanced Mineral Seasoning, and/or
  Bernard Jenson's Quick-Sip "Bouillon
  Concentrate" or seasoning (optional)
1 lg. or 2 sm. avocados

1. Wash and quarter tomatoes and place in blender, along with lemon or lime juice, and liquefy on highest blender speed.
2. Wash celery, cut off leaves, and cut into sixths.
3. With blender running on high speed, gradually add celery and continue blending until celery is liquefied.
4. Taste blender mixture. If it's too acid or bland, prepare and add more celery until it tastes GREAT.
5. Add seasoning(s) if you wish, to taste, and blend in.
6. Peel, quarter and add avocados and blend until smooth.

CREAMY LENTIL CASSEROLE * * * * *

For two servings:
Lentil sprouts
½ lemon
1 med. tomato
2 stalks celery
1 med. avocado

1. Pour sprouted lentils into salad bowls.
2. Juice lemon half and place in blender, along with washed and quartered tomato, and liquefy on high speed.
3. Wash celery, cut off leaves, cut into sixths, and gradually add through opening in blender lid while blender is running on high speed.
4. Quarter, peel and add avocado to running blender and liquefy until smooth and creamy.
5. Pour avocado-tomato sauce over lentil sprouts, mix well, and serve.

HEALTHFUL 'N' TASTY TACOS * * * * *

These tacos are exceptionally healthful because they are 100% raw and contain no meat, cheese, beans or condiments. And they taste *great!*

Whole lettuce leaves (Boston, Romaine,
  Bibb or Leaf)
Creamy ripe avocados
Flavorful tomatoes (add lemon juice if
  you can't get tasty tomatoes)
Cilantro (a relative of parsley,
  found in many supermarkets)
Alfalfa sprouts
Special Taco Sauce (see recipe below)

Taco ingredients can be served separately for each person to make his own, with the "chef" setting the example.

1. Wash and dry lettuce leaves and place on a platter.
2. Quarter and peel avocados; slice each quarter lengthwise twice; and place avocado slices on a plate.
3. With tomatoes sitting stem up, wash and cut into half-inch slices; then cut each slice into half-inch strips and place on a plate.

4. If you use lemon juice in addition to tomatoes, simply cut lemon into wedges and place on a plate. Or, if you prefer, you may juice lemons and place lemon juice in a small pitcher/creamer or bowl.
5. Wash cilantro, removing bad leaves as you go; cut off roots; place on cutting board; cut up finely; and put in a bowl.
6. Serve alfalfa sprouts in a bowl, also; and serve generous portions of Special Taco Sauce (recipe below) to each individual in cups or small bowls.
7. Assemble a taco while eaters watch and make their own along with you: Place a lettuce leaf on a large plate; then fill the center, lengthwise, with avocado strips, tomato strips, cut-up cilantro, taco sauce, alfalfa sprouts (and lemon juice, if you're using it) and fold each side of the lettuce leaf over and eat with your hands. It is a bit messy, so I recommend either cloth napkins, terry cloth hand towels, or (preferably) 100% cotton herringbone or waffle weave towels.

Special Taco Sauce

Shelled pecans
Tomatoes
Grapefruit
Lemon
Celery

1. Wash and quarter tomatoes and place in blender, along with juiced grapefruit (one-half for every one to two eaters) and lemon (about one-fourth per person).
2. Liquefy tomatoes in citrus juices on highest blender speed; wash celery, cut off leaves and cut into sixths; and, with blender running,, gradually add celery through opening in blender lid, blending until liquefied.
3. Taste blender mixture. If it's too acidic or too bland, prepare and add more celery, until it tastes *terrific*.
4. Then, with blender running on high speed, add pecans through opening in blender lid.
5. When mixture becomes too thick to blend, stop and start blender to get it going again. When that doesn't work, stop blender and stir contents before blending again, repeating as often as necessary. With blender stopped, stir in more tomato if more liquid is needed.

This sauce is neither hot nor spicy (condimented) because that would make it unhealthful (irritating to body cells and tissues). However, it is ultra-delicious, with a tomatoey flavor, so it is an excellent taco sauce nonetheless.

CHINESE STIR-FRY **

Brown rice
Distilled water
Cauliflower
Mung bean sprouts
Azuki bean sprouts
Bok choy
Cabbage
Collard Greens
Snow peas
Broccoli
Sweet peas
Green Beans

1. First make rice by boiling two parts distilled water and slowly adding one part brown rice. Cover pan and steam 25 minutes on low heat. Then, without removing the lid, turn off heat and allow to set another 15 minutes.
2. While rice is cooking, prepare your choice of any or all of the vegetables and sprouts, using those that are available fresh for maximum wholesomeness.
3. Steam vegetables in a very small amount of distilled water (without using a steamer rack).
4. Place rice on plates and serve steamed vegetables on top of rice. Very tasty!

An alternative to using strictly fresh vegetables is to use some frozen vegetables, along with the fresh vegetables. If you wish, you may use a frozen Oriental or Chinese vegetable mix, but keep in mind that they contain onions and mushrooms, which contain toxic components. If you prefer to use scallions and/or mushrooms despite their toxic components, fresh are somewhat less unwholesome than frozen.

Whether or not you use a frozen Oriental or Chinese vegetable mix, you may wish to use canned sliced or whole water chestnuts and/or canned bamboo shoots. (Canned foods, of course, are far less wholesome than fresh and also much less wholesome than frozen foods.)

An optional ingredient you may enjoy is tofu. Simply cube, stir-fry in another pan, and add at the end.

If you desire the oily flavor of real stir-frying over simply steaming your vegetables, steam the vegetables half the normal time and then drain off water, add a cold-pressed oil, and fry on medium-low heat, stirring continuously.

Also, you may use powdered or granular kelp and/or other nonsalt seasonings such as Bernard Jensen's Organic Seasoning and Instant Gravy and/or Nature's Gourmet seasoning. Soy sauce contains salt but may be used if desired. If you use seasonings, add them to the vegetables, either while stir-frying them or after steaming them.

Choose your ingredients and cooking methods according to the degree of health you are trying to achieve. If you are earnestly seeking perfect health, skip this recipe and stick to a raw foods diet. Others may compromise according to their individual values and health goals.

NUTRITIOUS NUT BUTTERS

Unroasted and unsalted nuts and seeds are delicious, wholesome protein- and nutrient-rich natural foods. In addition to providing readily usable, high-quality protein, raw nuts and seeds are superior sources of essential fatty acids; calcium, magnesium and other valuable minerals; and B-complex and other vitamins necessary to high-level body functioning. And on top of that, they're exceptionally delicious!

Nuts and seeds are also convenience foods of a sort, for they keep well without refrigeration, especially when still in their shells. In addition, they are concentrated, compact, and dry, so they are easy to carry in lunches, on trips, etc. Nuts and seeds can be easily stored in glass jars in your freezer or refrigerator, or even on shelves or in cupboards, depending upon how fast you use them and whether or not they're shelled.

The variety of wholesome nuts and seeds is quite extensive—another plus for nuts and seeds as basic items in a healthful diet. The tastiest nuts, in my opinion, are pecans. I also adore pistachios when I can get them unroasted and unsalted (not always easy, unfortunately). Though I love cashews, too, I get them only rarely because they are not edible when perfectly raw. (They must be slightly heated to dissipate the caustic carditic acid in the oil between the cashews' two shells. This is why they cannot be purchased in the shell.)

Other nutritious and tasty edible nuts and seeds commonly available include macadamia nuts (rich and delicious!), filberts (also known as hazelnuts), English walnuts, black walnuts, pumpkin seeds (pepitas), sesame seeds, sunflower seeds, almonds, and Brazil nuts. There are others, but these are the most commonly available in the U.S.

(Peanuts are not included among the wholesome nuts because, for one thing, they are a legume, not a nut. Also, they, like the other legumes, contain starch, in addition to much protein and oil. Since protein and starch digest poorly when consumed together, peanuts, even if eaten raw and unsalted, digest very poorly, resulting in toxic indigestion by-products.)

Not only are nuts and seeds extremely delicious, nutritious and convenient to eat, but they are also immensely satisfying, due to their high oil content. A vegetable/salad meal that includes up to four ounces of nuts or seeds daily (or at least three times weekly) helps insure a feeling of satiety, as well as plenty of nutrients. In addition, crunching on nuts and seeds is quite satisfying, and the chewing is excellent exercise—honestly!

Not only are nuts and seeds excellent in vegetable salads, salad dressings, and nut milks, but they are also excellent made into nut butters and used as is or used as lettuce leaf sandwich spreads, along with tomato slices, vegetables and sprouts. With the exceptionally delicious flavors of the various nut butters, you'll forget about peanut butter entirely!

Fresh Nut Butters Are Best!

My mother, like many other people I know, is a peanut butter lover. One day when we were shopping in a large natural foods store here in Austin, she was going to buy some peanut butter. First, I suggested that she buy unsalted peanut butter. Then I informed her that all peanut butter is made from roasted peanuts and that peanuts are unwholesome because they're hard to digest due to their high starch content.

I suggested that she purchase almond or sunflower butter instead, since these are more wholesome than peanut butter. These nut butters are fairly expensive, though, and bottled products are always far inferior to their fresh counterparts. As my mother was putting these jars of nut butters in her basket, I was thinking about how she could enjoy her food more and simultaneously eat better and save money.

Then it came to me. "Trudy," I said, "why don't you buy a Champion juicer and make your own nut butters fresh? They'll be tastier and more healthful than anything you can get in a jar, and you can have a wider variety to choose from, too. And, besides, you've been wanting a Champion so you can make banana ice cream for the grandkids!"

That did it! Trudy returned the jars of nut butters to the shelf and purchased a Champion juicer. Then she bought several bags of her favorite kinds of unroasted nuts and seeds. With the glee of a kid on Christmas morning, Trudy paid for her Champion, took it home, and proceeded to make delicious nut butters. She delightedly exclaimed to me, "The Champion is so easy to use and easy to clean!"

She has many times made banana ice cream for the grandkids, as well as all kinds of fresh juices. In addition, she has used her Champion to grate cabbage and carrots for homemade cole slaw. In short, Trudy's been immmensely delighted with her purchase—and so have the grandkids!

WALNUT BUTTER * * * * *

English walnuts

Put walnuts through a Champion juicer with the blank in place, or grind them up in an electric nut-and-seed grinder, a blender or a hand grinder. English walnuts are rich in nutritious natural oils, and they have an excellent nut buttery texture and flavor.

Be sure to use only the freshest of nuts and to eat immediately after making. If you must store Walnut Butter, do so in tightly-covered container for one to two days in a refrigerator (or longer in a freezer).

PECAN BUTTER * * * * *

This is one of the most exquisitely delicious nonfruit foods you'll ever want to taste. It's excellent with tomatoes!

Pecans

Put pecans through a Champion juicer with the juicer blank in place, or grind in a nut-and-seed grinder, a hand grinder or a blender. Texas native pecans are best because they are richer in natural oils and most flavorful, but other pecans are also extremely delicious.

Since pecans are one of the tastiest of the nuts, they make an out-of-this-world nut butter no other nut or seed can match. Serve freshly made for best flavor and nutrition, or store in a tightly-covered container in a refrigerator or freezer.

79

BRAZIL NUT BUTTER *****

Brazil nuts

Put Brazil nuts through a Champion juicer with the juicer blank in place, or grind in an electric nut and seed grinder, a hand grinder, or a blender and serve freshly made.

Brazils are extremely rich in natural oils, so no additional oil should be added. In fact, you may mix a little Brazil nut butter with other, dryer, nut butters if you wish. This is far more wholesome than adding free (fragmented) oils.

Note: If your Brazil nut butter doesn't taste absolutely terrific, it means your Brazil nuts were not fresh enough.

SUNFLOWER SEED BUTTER *****

Sunflower seeds, hulled

Simply put raw sunflower seeds through a Champion juicer (with the juicer blank in place), or grind them in an electric or hand nut and seed grinder or a blender and serve fresh.

Sunflower seeds are in the price range of peanuts, but their nutritive value and digestibility are miles more than peanuts, so they make an excellent substitute for peanut butter. Since sunflower seeds usually have a little less oil than English walnuts, pecans, or Brazil nuts, you may want to mix in a little of one of these nuts to add extra oils (Brazil nuts are best). Or you may mix sunflower seed butter (or any dry nut butter) with a little distilled water to obtain a moister texture.

As with the other nut butters, if you must store Sunflower Seed Butter, do so in a tightly-covered container in a refrigerator or freezer.

Nut Butters With Veggies

Most people are accustomed to eating peanut butter on bread or toast, or in cookies. Breads and cookies, however, like peanut butter, are unwholesome. So we need to find new, healthy, ways to eat nuts butters.

In fact, there is a superb way to eat freshly-made nut butters. This is to simply spread them on vegetables. The best vegetables to spread nut butters on are celery, cauliflower and broccoli. (If you wish, you may dip into or sprinkle with whole hulled sunflower seeds.) Fresh nut butters are also excellent on lettuce leaves (and why not add tomato slices and alfalfa sprouts while you're at it, and enjoy a super-good sandwich?). In fact, nut butters are great on most any fresh raw vegetable.

DELECTABLE PUDDINGS

Puddings have always been among my favorite foods because of their sweetness and their smooth, creamy texture. As a young child, I was always delighted when my grandma treated me and my brother to a jar of baby food because it was always so sweet and tasty. Now, of course, I know what was in that baby food, so I know why all my baby teeth, as well as all of my adult teeth, developed cavities. (How I wish my mother and grandma had read Dr. Herbert M. Shelton!)

Now adults, teenagers, children, and babies alike can enjoy the sweetness, deliciousness, and creamy-smoothness of many delightful yet wholesome puddings. Rather than healthful eating being a sacrifice of the things we love, it turns out to offer a wide variety of super-delicious, incredibly-wholesome natural foods.

Blenders are ideal for pudding-making (though many delectable puddings can be made with a fork or potato masher, a bowl, and a spoon). You can also use a Champion juicer for making puddings. Whatever equipment you use, you will no doubt find puddings to be highly-satisfying, nourishing, and exquisitely-delicious dishes that people of all ages will immensely enjoy.

SWEET CAROB PUDDING *****

Distilled water
Dates
Raw carob powder

1. Pour distilled water into blender; add pitted dates; and liquefy on high speed.
2. Stop blender; carefully add some carob powder; and blend again.
3. Continue stopping; adding carob powder; and blending until mixture is smooth, creamy, and somewhat thick.
4. If necessary, add more water, dates or carob as needed to obtain the desired sweetness, thickness and richness.
5. Let sit overnight in a refrigerator to set and thicken a bit more.

REVELOUS RAISIN PUDDING * * * * *

Monukka or Thompson raisins
Bananas

1. Soak raisins overnight or several hours in distilled water; then blend raisins, soak water and bananas together until well blended.
2. Turn blender off and on a few times to facilitate thorough blending, or, if necessary, turn off blender, stir, and blend again, repeating this one or more times as needed.
3. Serve plain or with the soaked raisins and/or sliced banana(s) on top. Marvelous!

PERFECT PLUM PUDDING * * * * *

Plums
Bananas, peeled and frozen

1. Wash and halve fresh plums; remove pits; place plums in blender; and liquefy on high speed.
2. With blender still running on high speed, add frozen peeled bananas through opening in blender lid, a half banana at a time, until mixture becomes thick, stopping blender and stirring when necessary.
3. You may use all or partly fresh bananas, but frozen bananas make the pudding thicker and colder.
4. Serve immediately—plain or with sliced bananas or other fresh fruit on top or mixed in. Outstanding!

EXTRAORDINARY BLUEBERRY PUDDING * * * * *

Ripe bananas
Fresh blueberries
Oranges (optional)

1. Peel bananas and liquefy on high blender speed until creamy.
2. If you wish, you may blend in a little freshly-made orange juice.
3. Pour mixture into bowls and wash blueberries, removing any that are green or mushy.
4. Stir in whole blueberries. Exquisite!

Note: I tried blending the blueberries with the bananas and orange juice. While it did create a lovely purple color and a tasty pudding, it wasn't nearly as de-luscious as with the blueberries left whole.

BANANA-PEACH PUDDING * * * * *

Ripe banana(s)
Fresh peaches

1. Peel very ripe banana(s) and break in half.
2. Place bananas in blender and liquefy on high speed.
3. Wash peaches; remove pits; add to blended bananas; and blend again on high speed until liquefied.
4. Serve with or without diced fresh and/or soaked dried fruit on top or mixed in.
5. This pudding is delectable and simple to prepare.

   Note: If you wish, you may use peeled and frozen bananas instead of or in addition to fresh bananas to make this pudding thicker and colder. If you use frozen bananas, liquefy peaches [and/or fresh bananas], first; then add frozen bananas through opening in blender lid while blender is running.

NECTAREAN NECTARINE PUDDING * * * * *

Fresh nectarines

1. Wash nectarines; remove pits; place fruit in blender; and liquefy on high speed until creamy and smooth. (Nectarines do not have to be peeled first, unless you want to peel off pesticides.)
2. Serve this pudding plain or with a few blueberries, soaked raisins (or other cut-up soaked dried fruit), sliced banana, or any other kind of diced fresh fruit on top or mixed in. (Nectarines, peaches, apricots, plums, grapes, and berries combine best with this pudding.)

TEMPTING SANDWICHES

Sandwiches are such standard fare in the traditional American diet that we seem to be naturally inclined to eat them—even if we don't include breads in our diet. Breads are difficult-to-digest conglomerations of mostly-toxic and unusable ingredients (wheat flour, other flours, yeast, salt, sweeteners, etc.), wheat being the foremost among these.

What's so toxic and unusable about wheat and wheat flour? Many things! For one, the gluten in wheat is indigestible because we don't have the enzyme to digest it. For another thing, wheat is deficient in the alkaline minerals and too rich in nitrogen and phosphoric acid. Thus it acidifies the system. Along this same vein, wheat is high in phytic acid, which tends to bind calcium, iron and zinc, making them unusable to the body. In addition, the starches in wheat (and other grains) are difficult to digest (about ten times more difficult than potato starch) and are thus prone to fermentation. And, because grains are so high in starch, we, with only one starch-splitting enzyme, ptyalin, are not capable of adequately digesting grains. Fermenting starches result in a host of toxic, disease- and sickness-causing fermentation by-products.

In addition to the problems of bread itself, the foods eaten in sandwiches (proteins, sugars) are generally poor digestive combinations with starch. Thus there is this additional digestive complication. Foods that are not digested efficiently are toxic in the body. In addition, the body is deprived of nutrients, and the toxic burden within further interferes with digestion of foods and assimilation of nutrients. Thus bread-and-sandwich-eating impairs nutrition.

Fortunately, there are ways to enjoy sandwiches without eating bread. Whole washed lettuce leaves, particularly Romaine lettuce and Leaf lettuce, make an excellent, low-calorie substitute for breads. And, unlike most other vegetables, lettuce combines very well with, fruits, vegetables, proteins and starches. You can also use other edible green leaves such as cabbages, bok choy, collards, etc., or even whole or halved bell peppers, celery stalks, etc., for making sandwiches.

For some unknown reason, most people find sandwiches made with fruits or vegetables to be great fun to eat, as well as especially delicious. Try out some of the following sample recipes, and see if you don't discover this to be the case for you, your family, and your friends, too!

BANANA SANDWICHES *****

Lettuce
Bananas
Raisins or dates

1. Wash and dry lettuce leaves; peel and halve bananas; and slice banana halves lengthwise.
2. Place banana slices down the middle of lettuce leaves and top with soaked or dry raisins or pitted dates.
3. Add a fruit dressing, sauce or pudding, if you wish.
4. Fold over each slide and eat like a sandwich. This requires manual dexterity, but the results are delicious!

VEGGIE-NORI FOLD-UP ****

Romaine lettuce
Chinese cabbage
Red bell pepper
Avocado
Nori

1. Wrap a peeled avocado quarter and a washed red pepper half in nori.
2. Wrap a washed cabbage leaf around the whole thing, making the fold opposite the nori fold.
3. Finally, wrap a washed lettuce leaf around the whole thing, folding on one of the open sides.

BRAZIL BUTTER HANDWICHES *****

Brazil nuts
Celery
Lettuce
Tomatoes and/or lemon juice

1. Put Brazil nuts through a Champion juicer (with the juicer blank in place), or grind in an electric or manual nut and seed grinder or in a blender.
2. Wash and finally dice celery; wash and dry whole (Romaine, Leaf or Boston) lettuce leaves; and wash and dice tomatoes (and/or juice lemon).
3. Place nut butter and diced celery on lettuce leaves; add tomatoes and/or lemon juice; and eat with your hands.

AVOCADO HANDWICHES *****

Lettuce (Romaine, Leaf or Boston)
Avocado(s)
Tomatoes
Alfalfa sprouts

1. Wash and dry lettuce; quarter and peel avocado(s); slice each avocado quarter twice lengthwise; and wash tomatoes and slice into narrow strips.
2. Place avocado and tomato slices lengthwise down the middle of lettuce leaves; add sprouts; and eat with your hands.

OPEN-FACED EGGPLANT SANDWICHES *****

Eggplant(s)
Boston lettuce
Red bell peppers
Avocados

1. De-stem and peel eggplant. Taste to make sure it's not bitter. (If it is, steam it and use in a cooked eggplant recipe.) If eggplant isn't bitter, slice it horizontally into ¾" thick circles.
2. Wash lettuce and red bell peppers; de-seed and cut up peppers; and quarter, peel, and slice or mash avocados.
3. Make open-faced sandwiches using eggplant slices as your "bread." Place sliced or mashed avocado on eggplant slices; then place red bell peppers and a couple leaves of Boston lettuce on top and enjoy!

SUPERB SOUPS

Soups, like sandwiches, are among the most popular of all foods. The reasons are anyone's guess. Perhaps their lightness makes them popular; or maybe it's their simplicity. In the wintertime, hot soups are appealing as a warm-up food; and, being very liquid, cool or cold soups can be quite appropriate for those hot summer days.

Though it is preferable not to use liquids with whole foods since they tend to dilute our digestive juices, soups can round out a meal nicely. (Or, you may make a soup a meal in itself.)

Most soups, especially those in cans or packages, are far too salty, as well as loaded with a plethora of other irritating condiments. Salt and other seasonings are used to make soups tasty. However, as with other natural foods, the ingredients used in wholesome soups are tasty in and of themselves, particularly when the ingredients are combined to obtain maximum flavor. If you wish, you can use salt-free vegetable seasonings, though these are not recommended for use on a regular basis because they pervert the taste buds and, at least to some degree, irritate body cells and tissues.

The following sample recipes include some fruit soups and some vegetable soups. Any of the vegetable soups can be heated a bit, if you wish, though this practice is discouraged since heat rapidly and readily destroys nutrients and flavor. All you need for most soups is a blender, so go to it!

BLUEBERRY SOUP *****

**Blueberries, fresh or
  frozen and thawed**
Fresh pear(s)
½-1 banana

1. Wash blueberries and discard any green or mushy ones; quarter, peel and core pear(s); and peel and halve banana(s).
2. Blend all ingredients on highest blender speed and serve.

BANANA SOUP * * *

For two servings:
6-10 bananas
1-½ c. unsweetened coconut
1-½ c. raisins

1. Liquefy bananas on highest blender speed and pour into a saucepan.
2. Stir in shredded or grated coconut (fresh coconut can be put through a Champion juicer with the juicer blank in place).
3. While heating the mixture a bit, add and stir in raisins.
4. Heat only until warm.
5. Slice another banana on top if desired.

LAURA'S PAPAYA SOUP * * * * *

Ripe papaya(s)
Frozen ripe bananas

1. Peel and freeze ripe bananas in plastic bags.
2. Halve papaya(s) and scoop out seeds with a spoon. Then scoop out flesh from skins into a blender.
3. Make banana ice cream by putting frozen bananas through a Champion juicer with the juicer blank in place; add ice cream to blender; and blend just enough to mostly mix banana ice cream with papaya(s), stopping blender and stirring with a spoon if necessary.
4. Serve immediately. Incredibly delicious!

VELVETY MELON SOUP *****

Ripe Honeydew and/or
  Scharlyn (Israel) melon(s)
Watermelon and/or cantaloupe
  (optional)

1. Halve and remove seeds from Honeydew and/or Scharlyn melon(s); slice each half into 1-½" strips; and peel each strip with a sharp knife.
2. Place one peeled melon slice in blender and liquefy on high speed.
3. Remove centerpiece from blender lid and add remaining melon slices, one at a time, holding the palm of your hand over the opening after each addition.
4. Replace centerpiece and continue blending for a couple of minutes until smooth and frothy.
5. Pour blender contents into soup bowls.
6. If you wish, you may dice some seeded watermelon and/or cantaloupe into bite-size pieces and stir into liquid mixture.

  This soup is refreshing and captivatingly sweet, aromatic and flavorful!

BANANA CREAM SOUP *****

Ripe bananas
Fresh pineapple

1. Blend approximately equal amounts of ripe bananas with fresh pineapple on highest blender speed for a few minutes, or until creamy and smooth.
2. Serve in soup bowls.

CRUNCHY CASHEW-CARROT SOUP *****

To make two servings:
6-8 oz. raw cashew pieces
12-16 carrots

1. Wash carrots and prepare for juicing by cutting into pieces that will fit through juicer mouth.
2. Juice carrots and place juice in blender.
3. Add about two-thirds of cashews and liquefy on high speed for a minute or two; then pour blender contents into a soup bowl.
4. Add remaining cashew pieces to bowls and stir.

This tasty soup is excellent alongside a vegetable salad.

BROCCOLI SOUP *****

For two servings:
Broccoli
Celery
Carrots
Sunflower seeds

1. Use broccoli steamed, raw, or part steamed and part raw. If you use steamed broccoli, wash it and steam four minutes on low heat (after starting steam on high heat).
2. Cut up broccoli and place in a large mixing bowl.
3. Wash celery and carrots, using twice as much celery as carrots; juice carrots and celery; and place in blender, along with about two ounces of sunflower seeds per serving.
4. Liquefy on high speed and pour into large bowl of broccoli.
5. Stir and serve with a soup ladle. Excellent alongside any vegetable salad!

CARROT SOUP * * * * *

Carrots, lots (the major ingredient)
Celery, about ½ stalk per serving
Parsley, two sprigs per serving
Avocados, about one per serving

1. Scrub and prepare most of the carrots for juicing; juice carrots; and pour juice into blender.
2. Wash celery and parsley; add to blender; and liquefy on high speed.
3. Halve and pit avocados; scoop flesh into blender; liquefy until smooth and creamy; and pour into soup bowls.
4. Grate remaining carrots with a hand grater, in a Champion juicer, or in a food processor.
5. Stir grated carrots into soup bowls and serve.
6. A few lightly-steamed peas may be mixed in if desired.
   Excellent as a meal in itself or served alongside a vegetable salad.

CREAM OF TOMATO SOUP * * * * *

For two servings:
4 tomatoes
4 tomatillos (if available)
  or juice of ½ lemon or lime
6-8 sprigs fresh parsley
3 stalks celery
6-8 oz. pignolia nuts

1. Wash, halve and liquefy tomatoes in blender.
2. Wash and halve tomatillos (or juice ½ lemon or lime) and add to blender, along with washed parsley.
3. Wash celery and cut stalks into fourths.
4. Place celery in blender with pignolia nuts and liquefy on high speed until creamy.
5. Serve in large soup bowls.
6. If desired, diced celery and/or whole pignolia nuts may be added and stirred in, as well as other fresh chopped vegetables. Or lettuce leaves, broccoli or other vegetables may be dunked into soup.

TERRIFIC TRANSITION RECIPES

Transition recipes are recipes that, while not optimally healthful, are far more wholesome than their conventional counterparts. They are called such because they help people make the transition from traditional fare to more wholesome fare gradually instead of suddenly.

However, there are some liabilities to using transition recipes too heavily. For one thing, some people may not experience pronounced health benefits if they use too many transition recipes. Others stay "in transition" and do not move on to a yet more wholesome dietary, and this, too, is unfortunate.

Nonetheless, transition recipes can have a place in the diets of those who are not psychologically able or willing to change over to an optimum diet at once. Many people do find it easy, even exciting, though, to switch directly from a conventional dietary to optimum fare, without a transition phase.

And, contrary to popular opinion (which is often wrong), it is not dangerous or bad to go right from consuming traditional fare to eating an all- or mostly-raw Hygienic diet. In fact, the health benefits may be so noticeable when a sudden transition is made that the individual is highly motivated to continue in his improved eating habits. It is simply not true that you are bound to backslide if you don't make the transition gradually (though some people do backslide, no matter how quickly or slowly they alter their dietary practices).

Some claim you may detoxify too fast if you change your diet too suddenly. However, this idea is totally fallacious, too, for the body never acts except in its own best interests. Your organism will not detoxify faster than it can healthfully handle. To think that it may is to subscribe to the seriously-mistaken medical concept that the body acts against itself. It does not! It acts only in self-defense against unwholesome substances and influences, but never to its own detriment. As long as you realize the truth of this fact, and understand that you may experience body elimination/cleansing/detoxification symptoms when you improve your diet, but that these symptoms are beneficial and will not hurt you, you will not fear changing over to the healthiest dietary possible as quickly as you wish.

The following recipes are less harmful than their conventional counterparts because they contain no sugar, honey, salt (sodium chloride, as from rocks and the sea), refined ingredients, or animal products (except unsalted butter, in the tortillas). They also use lemon or lime juice instead of vinegar, and the condiments used are salt-free herbal seasonings.

No doubt you will find the recipes in this section to be as delicious as anything you could want to eat, so, if you want to prepare foods that, though not perfect, are delicious and more wholesome than the foods traditionally eaten, try these!

Note: Many of the recipes elsewhere in this book are also transitional. These are rated as such with four-, three-, two-, or one-star ratings. Five-star recipes contain only optimum foods compatibly combined.

UNCOOKED VEGETARIAN MAYONNAISE #1 * * * *

Almonds
Distilled water
Lemon(s)
Seasoning(s), (paprika, ground mustard
 seed, Dr. Bronner's Balanced Mineral
 Seasoning, Nature's Gourmet herbal
 seasoning, and/or Bernard Jensen's
 Organic Seasoning and Instant Gravy, etc.)

1. Use blanched almonds, or blanch your own by pouring very hot or boiling water over almonds and then pinching the skins off between your thumb and index finger.
2. Place blanched almonds in blender, along with some distilled water, and liquefy on high speed until well blended, adding more water as needed, but keeping the mixture as thick as possible.
3. When almonds are well blended, add seasonings to taste and blend again. (To make this a five-star recipe, you may leave out the seasonings.)
4. Juice lemon(s); add lemon juice to taste; and blend once more. This will thicken the mixture.
5. Serve with fresh vegetables or fruits as a salad dressing, as an ingredient in other salad dressings, or as a vegetable dip or sandwich spread base.

UNCOOKED VEGETARIAN MAYONNAISE #2 ***

Almonds
Distilled water
Seasonings (as listed above in
  Uncooked Vegetarian Mayonnaise #1
Cold-pressed safflower oil
Lemon(s)

1. As in Uncooked Vegetarian Mayonnaise #1, use blanched almonds or blanch your own (see instruction for blanching in previous recipe), but use fewer almonds.
2. Place almonds in blender; add about twice to three times as much distilled water as almonds; and liquefy on high speed until well blended.
3. With blender running on high speed, very gradually add a little safflower oil at a time, until you've used about twice as much oil as nut milk.
4. Then add seasonings to taste; blend again; juice lemon(s) and add lemon juice to taste; and blend in lemon juice.
5. Serve in potato salad, cole slaw, vegetable or fruit salad dressings, etc., or use as a vegetable dip, a soup base (with tomatoes, celery, etc.), or a gravy.

TASTY TOMATO SAUCE *

A large quantity of fresh (meaty)
  tomatoes, preferably
  Italian Plum tomatoes
A few dates
Celery stalks
Onions or scallions, to taste
A little cold-pressed
  vegetable oil
A generous amount of fresh
  basil leaves (or dried
  sweet basil)
A little Nature's Gourmet (or
  other salt-free herbal seasoning)
A little Bernard Jenson's Organic
  Seasoning and Instant Gravy
  (optional)

1. Wash and halve tomatoes and press through a sieve or colander.
2. Let tomatoes stand awhile (until pulp settles); then pour off liquid and place tomato pulp in blender.
3. Pit dates; place in blender; and liquefy on high speed with tomato pulp.
4. Wash celery and cut off leaves; dice celery, add to blender, and liquefy.
5. Pour tomato pulp mixture into a cooking pan, along with finely-diced onion(s) or scallions, cold-pressed vegetable oil, and seasonings. Since basil is the most important seasoning in this recipe, use about four times as much basil as all the other seasonings combined. (Finely cut up fresh basil leaves if you use them.)
6. Bring mixture to a boil; then lower heat and simmer 20-35 minutes.

Excellent on or in whole wheat, soy or buckwheat spaghetti, noodles, pizza, lasagna, eggplant parmigiana, brown rice, stuffed peppers, etc.

BASIC BREADING *

4 c. whole wheat bread crumbs
½ c. whole wheat pastry flour
¼ c. fine corn meal
1-2 t. Nature's Gourmet, other
  salt-free herbal seasoning,
  Bernard Jensen's Organic
  Seasoning and Instant Gravy,
  and/or Vege-sal
1-2 t. paprika

1. Stir all ingredients together in a large bowl.
2. Use for breading vegetables.
3. Store extra breading in a covered jar.

EGGPLANT PARMIGIANA ULTIMA *

For two servings:
1 lg. or 2 sm. eggplant(s)
A little cold-pressed vegetable oil
Tasty Tomato Sauce (recipe above)
Appr. 1 c. peas, fresh or frozen
2 lg., 3 med. or 4 sm. tomatoes
  washed and diced
1 red (or green) bell
  pepper, washed and diced
1 med. turnip, peeled and
  finely diced
1 bunch wash and chopped scallions
2 cups diced tofu

1. De-stem, peel and slice eggplant in about ¾" thick rounds; brush both sides with oil; cover with Basic Breading (recipe above); and broil each side until tender, about 8-10 minutes, on lightly-oiled (or stick-free) cookie sheet.

2. Steam peas on low heat about four minutes (after starting steam on high heat).

3. Make Tasty Tomato Sauce (recipe above) and stir in steamed peas.

4. Lightly oil a flat baking dish; pour in a little tomato sauce; lay half the broiled eggplant slices on bottom of baking dish; and add half the diced tomatoes, diced peppers, chopped scallions, and tofu chunks.

5. Cover this first layer with half of your Tasty Tomato Sauce; then layer on remaining eggplant slices, tomatoes, peppers, turnips, scallions and tofu and cover with remaining tomato sauce.

6. Bake uncovered in a moderate oven about 25 minutes, until heated through and slightly browned.

7. Serve as the main course, alongside a light vegetable salad.

THICK, CREAMY SUMMER SQUASH SOUP * * *

For two servings:

**Equal amounts of cubed zucchini and
  yellow crookneck squash (or
  just one or the other), enough
  to fill a steamer rack** *very full*
7-8 stalks celery
2″-wedge of green cabbage
12 carrots
2 avocados
¼ c. dulse or 3 T. kelp
Nature's Gourmet (optional)

1. Wash squashes; dice into bite-sized chunks; place in a steamer rack; and steam 8-10 minutes, until done.
2. Meanwhile, wash and finely dice cabbage and one stalk of celery per person and place in a large mixing bowl.
3. Wash carrots and remaining celery; make carrot-celery juice; and place juice in blender.
4. Rinse dulse under cold water to remove salt; add dulse (or kelp) to blender; and liquefy on high speed.
5. Quarter and peel avocados; add to blender and liquefy on high speed until smooth and creamy.
6. Place steamed squashes and blender ingredients in large mixing bowl with the celery and cabbage and mix well. Extra kelp or Nature's Gourmet can be sprinkled into individual serving bowls, as desired by eaters.
7. This soup can be eaten alone or served alongside a vegetable salad or plate of washed lettuce leaves.

PERFECT POTATO SOUP WITH BROCCOLI ***

For 2-3 servings:
3 lg. or 4 sm. red potatoes
2 bn. celery
Half as many carrots as celery
2 bn. broccoli
Lots of mustard greens

1. Wash potatoes and steam whole 15-20 minutes.
2. While potatoes are steaming, wash all other ingredients; prepare celery and carrots for juicing; and set aside for juicing later.
3. Cut up broccoli and place in a large mixing bowl.
4. When potatoes are finished steaming, place them on a cutting board and steam mustard greens for two minutes.
5. Halve potatoes lengthwise so they cool quickly; place steamed mustard greens on a cutting board and slice in both directions to make somewhat small pieces; place greens in mixing bowl; dice up potatoes; and add to bowl.
6. Finally, juice celery and carrots; pour juice into mixing bowl; stir well and serve in soup bowls with a soup ladle. Primo!

CHINESE STIR-FRY #2 *

This recipe is rated one star because it is cooked in oil; it utilizes three incompatible food combinations; and it calls for soy sauce, which contains salt. Liabilities aside, it tastes terrific! (For a more wholesome version, see the section on Main-Course Meals.)

One part brown rice
Two parts distilled water

1. Bring water to a boil over high heat; slowly add rice; cover pan; and steam on low heat for 25 minutes.
2. Then, without removing lid, turn off heat and allow to set for another 15 minutes.

To make a sauce for this stir-fry, you will need a blender plus the following ingredients.

Distilled water
Pitted dates
Raw sesame tahini
Soy sauce

1. Blend dates with distilled water on high speed of blender for a few minutes.
2. Add soy sauce and tahini and continue blending, adding additional amounts of all ingredients until a desirable combination of sweetness and saltiness is obtained, along with a desirable texture and thickness.

While rice is cooking, prepare your choice of some or all of the following vegetables:

Broccoli
Mung bean sprouts
Mushrooms
Scallions
Azuki bean sprouts
Bok choy
Cabbage
Collard greens
Snow peas
Sweet peas
Cauliflower
Green beans
Bamboo shoots
Water chestnuts

You will also need:

**Almonds, raw or roasted; slivered,
  sliced or chopped (optional)**
Tofu, cubed
Cold-pressed oil
**Bernard Jensen's Organic Seasoning
  and Instant Gravy**
**Nature's Gourmet (or other
  salt-free seasoning)**
Kelp, powdered or granulated

1. Lightly steam vegetables; then drain off water, remove lid, and add oil to bottom of pan.
2. Next, fry vegetables and almonds in oil, stirring constantly. Mix in seasonings while stir-frying. If you use almonds, be careful not to use too many—just enough to give an occasional crunchy surprise.
3. Serve rice in bowls and put stir-fried vegetables on top. Then add sauce and stir ingredients in each individual bowl.

Note: A bottle of soy sauce may be put on the table for those who want extra. However, it probably won't be used because there is soy sauce in the sauce you've already mixed in.

HOMEMADE LASAGNA NOODLES **

1 part unbleached white flour
1 part whole wheat flour
1 part warm distilled water

1. Mix ingredients together well; shape into a ball; and knead lightly.
2. With a rolling pin, roll into a rectangular shape about 1/8" thick on a floured board; and sprinkle and smooth a little flour over both sides.
3. Beginning at the wide end, fold over 3" and then fold over 3 more inches on top of the first layer until dough is folded to one 3"-piece of several thicknesses.
4. Cut 1-½" strips and slowly drop into boiling water, one noodle at a time, keeping water boiling.
5. Cook about 7 minutes, stirring occasionally.
6. Drain on colander.

LUSCIOUS LASAGNA*

Lasagna noodles (see recipe
  above for homemade noodles)
Tofu, diced
Tasty Tomato Sauce (see recipe
  earlier in this section)
Basic Breading (optional)
  (see recipe earlier in this section)
Steamed peas (optional)
Fresh tomatoes
Other diced fresh or steamed
  vegetables of your choice

1. Preheat oven at 350 degrees; then, if you're using them, mix steamed peas into Tasty Tomato Sauce.
2. Place some tomato sauce in bottom of a Pyrex pan; layer on strips of lasagna noodles side by side; and cover with lots of tofu, diced tomatoes, other diced vegetables (if you're using them), and more suace.
3. Repeat, this time laying lasagna noodle in the other direction, then adding tofu, diced tomatoes, (diced vegetables), and more sauce.
4. Continue adding layers until pan is full; sprinkle with a little Basic Breading, if you wish; and bake about an hour.
5. Place lasagna on a cooling rack; cut into squares; and serve alongside a fresh vegetable salad.

VEGETARIAN PIZZA *

Crust:
2 c. whole wheat pastry flour
½ c. cold-pressed vegetable oil
¼ c. distilled water

Topping:
Tasty Tomato Sauce (see recipe,
   this chapter)
Tomatoes
Red or green peppers
Tofu
Oregano
Alfalfa sprouts (optional)

1. Preheat oven to 450 degrees.
2. Mix crust ingredients together and roll out to desired size.
3. Place on a lightly-greased pizza pan or cookie sheet and add tomato sauce and washed and diced fresh tomatoes.
4. Dice and saute peppers and tofu in a little cold-pressed vegetable oil and add to pizza, along with a sprinkling of oregano.
5. Bake about 10 minutes, until crust is brown.
6. Serve with alfalfa sprouts on top (if desired).

VEGGIE SPAGHETTI *

Tasty Tomato Sauce (see
  recipe in this chapter)
Tomatoes
Red or green peppers
Mushrooms (optional)
Oregano
Whole wheat spaghetti noodles

1. Wash, dice and saute peppers (and mushrooms, if you're using them) in a little cold-pressed vegetable oil.
2. Wash and dice fresh tomatoes and stir together Tasty Tomato Sauce, diced tomatoes, sauted peppers (and mushrooms), and oregano to taste.
3. Boil distilled water and then add spaghetti noodles.
4. Continue boiling 8-12 minutes, stirring occasionally.
5. Drain spaghetti noodles in a colander, pouring some distilled water over them to prevent sticking.
6. Serve spaghetti noodles and sauce separately, or served pre-mixed, depending upon your preference.

SESAME-OAT PANCAKES *

Fruit Topping:
Dates
Fresh fruit juice or
  distilled water
One or more kinds of
  fresh fruit(s)

Batter:
Appr. 4 c. distilled water
1 c. hulled sesame seeds
3 T. cold-pressed vegetable oil
1-½ c. cornmeal
1-½ c. quick oats

1. First make fruit topping by liquefying some pitted dates in a little fresh fruit juice or distilled water.
2. Wash and cut up fresh fruit into bowl; add date blend; mix well; and set aside.
3. To make batter, liquefy sesame seeds in half the distilled water.
4. When smooth, add oil, cornmeal, oats, and remaining water and blend together well.
5. Preheat lightly-oiled griddle or frying pan; spoon batter onto pan; and cook until small bubbles appear.
6. Then turn pancakes over; cook until done; and serve with very generous quantities of fruit topping.

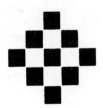